BOOK 3

PATTERNS IN SPELLING

Patterns with Consonant Blends and Digraphs

TIM BROWN

DEBORAH F. KNIGHT

NEW READERS PRESS
Publishing Division of Laubach Literacy International
Syracuse, New York

About the Authors

Deborah Knight began her teaching career in the early 1970s and has taught both reading and English in urban, suburban, and rural settings. Since 1984, Ms. Knight has served as the Coordinator of the Learning Disabilities Assistance Program at Onondaga Community College in Syracuse, New York. Working closely with these OCC students, she has helped them to develop strategies for improving their reading, writing, spelling, and study skills.

Tim Brown has worked with developing and remedial readers and writers since 1978. He teaches courses in spelling as well as freshman composition and literature at Onondaga Community College. He also serves as Senior Professional Tutor at the college's Writing Skills Center, where he has a special interest in teaching spelling to developing and remedial writers and ESL students.

ON THE COVER: A quilt entitled *Rhythm/Color: Morris Men*; 99½" x 99½", by Michael James. This work of art appeared in *The Art Quilt* exhibit and book of the same name. It is reproduced here through the courtesy of The Quilt Digest Press.

ISBN 0-88336-104-3

© 1990

New Readers Press
Publishing Division of Laubach Literacy International
Box 131, Syracuse, New York 13210

Printed in the United States of America

Project Editor: Christina M. Jagger
Manuscript Editor: Mary Hutchison
Illustrations by Christine Patsos-Kocak
Cover by Chris Steenwerth
Composition by Anne Hyde
Layout Artist: Joanne Groth

9 8 7 6 5 4 3

Table of Contents

Lesson 1

The Blends *bl*, *cl*, *fl*, *gl*, and *pl*

Sight Words		
million	iron	America
billion	house	century

Blends

1 Listening

bl

Listen to the sound of *bl* in these words.

black	blend	blame	blue
bless	blank	blaze	blow
bluff	blanket	blotch	blown

cl

Listen to the sound of *cl* in these words.

clap	class	claim
clip	clock	clean
cliff	clutch	clear

fl

Listen to the sound of *fl* in these words.

flag	fling	flame	fly
flat	flock	flare	flee
fled	fluid	flight	fleet

gl

Listen to the sound of *gl* in these words.

glad	glow	glare
glass	glue	gleam
glove	glum	glide

pl

Listen to the sound of *pl* in these words.

plan	place	explain	reply
pledge	plane	complain	employ
plenty	please	complete	explore

2 **Writing Words.** On the lines below, write the words that you hear.

1. _____   4. _____   7. _____

2. _____   5. _____   8. _____

3. _____   6. _____   9. _____

3 **Dictionary Skills: Alphabetizing.** On the lines below, alphabetize the words in Exercise 2.

1. _____   4. _____   7. _____

2. _____   5. _____   8. _____

3. _____   6. _____   9. _____

4 **Review of One-Syllable Word Patterns.** Review the following patterns that were covered in Books 1 and 2 of this series. On the lines provided, write words from Exercise 1 that are examples of each pattern.

Pattern: A one-syllable word with a long vowel sound often ends in silent *e*.

1. _____   3. _____   5. _____

2. _____   4. _____   6. _____

Pattern: When one-syllable words with a short vowel end with the sounds /f/, /l/, or /s/, the final sound is usually spelled *ff*, *ll*, or *ss*.

1. _____   3. _____   5. _____

2. _____   4. _____

Pattern: The letters *ck* are usually used to spell the sound /k/ at the end of a one-syllable word with a short vowel.

1. _____   2. _____   3. _____

Pattern: The letters *tch* are usually used to spell the sound /ch/ at the end of a one-syllable word with a short vowel.

1. _____   2. _____

5 **Review of Syllable Types.** In Book 2 of this series, you learned to identify five types of syllables. Review these syllable types and write one example of each type on the lines below.

1. A **closed** syllable ends with a short vowel followed by one or more consonants.

2. An **open** syllable ends with a vowel that is usually long.

3. A **Cle** syllable has a consonant plus *le* and usually comes at the end of a word.

4. A **VCe** syllable has a long vowel followed by a consonant and ends in a silent *e*.

5. A **double vowel** syllable has two vowels together that make one sound.

Syllable Type	Example	Your Example
1. Closed	set	_____
2. Open	re	_____
3. Cle	ble	_____
4. VCe	ake	_____
5. Double Vowel	eem	_____

6 **Writing Words with Cle Syllables.** The consonant pairs in Exercise 1 of this lesson are often used in Cle syllables. When *bl, cl, fl, gl,* and *pl* are used to form Cle syllables, they are not pronounced as blends. For example, *ble* is pronounced /bŭl/ or /bəl/. Write the words you hear, which all end in Cle syllables.

1. _____   4. _____   7. _____

2. _____   5. _____   8. _____

3. _____   6. _____   9. _____

7 **The Possessive Apostrophe.** When something belongs to someone or something, use an apostrophe (') to show ownership or possession. Follow the steps below.

Step 1: Write the owner(s) or possessor(s).

      a boy   the clocks
      the class   the children

Step 2: Add an apostrophe.

      a boy'   the clocks'
      the class'   the children'

Step 3: Add an *s* if you can hear one when you say the phrase.

      a boy's best friend   the clocks' hands
      the class's field trips   the children's playground

Rewrite the phrases below to show possession.

1. the wings of the airplanes   _____

2. the bicycle of Uncle John   _____

3. the leaves of the trees   _____

4. the clothes of Chris   _____

5. the color of the glass   _____

6. the choice of the people   _____

8 **Writing Sentences.** On the lines below, write the sentences that you hear.

1. _____

2. _____

3. _____

4. _____

5. _____

Lesson 2

The Blends *br*, *cr*, *fr*, and *gr*

Sight Words		
bruise	suit	build
cruise	fruit	juice

Blends

① Listening

br

Listen to the sound of *br* in these words.

brick	braid	brave	library
bridge	brain	broke	February
brush	brake	broken	breakfast

cr

Listen to the sound of *cr* in these words.

crop	crack	crazy	cry
cross	cradle	cream	creep
crossing	crankcase	creek	crayon

fr

Listen to the sound of *fr* in these words.

free	frog	frame	Friday
freeze	frost	afraid	France
froze	friend	fright	San Francisco

gr

Listen to the sound of *gr* in these words.

grab	grade	agree	grapes
grand	grain	green	grease
grill	grave	greet	griddle

② Writing Words. On the lines below, write the words that you hear.

1. _____   4. _____   7. _____

2. _____   5. _____   8. _____

3. _____   6. _____   9. _____

3 **Review of Syllable Types.** Write each syllable below on a line under the correct heading. The first one has been done to get you started.

√froze	cra	green	braid	ble
grab	brake	bri	gle	cross
fro	ple	frame	grease	brick

Closed

1. _____
2. _____
3. _____

Open

1. _____
2. _____
3. _____

Cle

1. _____
2. _____
3. _____

VCe

1. _froze_____
2. _____
3. _____

Double Vowel

1. _____
2. _____
3. _____

4 **Writing Words by Syllables.** Write each word your teacher dictates by syllables. Then write the whole word on the line provided.

First Syllable	Second Syllable	Third Syllable	Fourth Syllable	Whole Word
1. _____	_____			_____
2. _____	_____			_____
3. _____	_____	_____		_____
4. _____	_____	_____		_____
5. _____	_____	_____	_____	_____
6. _____	_____	_____	_____	_____

5 **Distinguishing Between *cr* and *gr*.** Underline the syllable you hear.

1. crid — grid   5. crad — grad   9. cruz — gruz

2. crel — grel   6. crim — grim   10. craf — graf

3. cron — gron   7. crep — grep

4. crub — grub   8. crot — grot

6 **Using Words with *r* Blends.** On the lines below, write the words that you hear.

1. _____ 2. _____ 3. _____

Use each of these words in sentences of your own.

1. _____

2. _____

3. _____

7 **Word Building: Compound Words.** Form the compound words indicated below. All of these compounds are closed.

1. grape + fruit   _____   5. brain + storm   _____

2. friend + ship   _____   6. frost + bite   _____

3. draw + bridge   _____   7. out + cry   _____

4. grand + mother   _____   8. griddle + cake   _____

Write three compound words formed with each of the words below. The given words can be at either the beginning or the end of the compound words, for example, *greenhouse* and *evergreen*. Use your dictionary to see if your compounds are closed, hyphenated, or open.

1. cross   _____ _____ _____

2. free   _____ _____ _____

3. green   _____ _____ _____

8 **Doubling Pattern 1.** Review Doubling Pattern 1, which was introduced in Book 1 of this series, and follow the directions below.

Pattern: Double the final consonant if a word has one syllable, one vowel, and one final consonant, and the ending begins with a vowel. Do not double *w* or *x*.

1. Look at each word below. If the word has one syllable, one vowel, or one final consonant, check the appropriate box. If you check all three boxes and the ending begins with a vowel, double the final consonant before adding the ending. Do not double *w* or *x*.

2. If you do not check all three boxes or the ending begins with a consonant, do not double the final consonant. Write the word on the line provided.

	One syllable	One vowel	One final consonant		
1. grill				+ ed	_____
2. grab				+ ing	_____
3. brag				+ ed	_____
4. free				+ dom	_____
5. flood				+ ed	_____
6. brush				+ ing	_____
7. flex				+ ible	_____
8. grin				+ ing	_____

9 **Writing Sentences.** On the lines below, write the sentences that you hear.

1. _____

2. _____

3. _____

4. _____

5. _____

Lesson 3

The Blends *pr*, *tr*, and *dr*

Sight Words		
salad	chocolate	food
onion	spaghetti	refrigerator

Blends

1 Listening

pr

Listen to the sound of *pr* in these words.

pray	pretty	price	April
praise	problem	pride	improve
preach	present	prize	practice
program	president	surprise	preparing

tr

Listen to the sound of *tr* in these words.

trap	track	train	pantry
trip	trick	treat	country
trim	truck	truly	entrance
tree	trade	travel	tragedy

dr

Listen to the sound of *dr* in these words.

drag	drop	dry	dream
drug	dress	drive	hundred
drum	address	drove	children

2 Writing Words. On the lines below, write the words that you hear.

1. _____   5. _____   9. _____

2. _____   6. _____   10. _____

3. _____   7. _____   11. _____

4. _____   8. _____   12. _____

3 **Word Building.** Write the missing syllable of each word you hear.

1. _____ blem   4. _____ trance   7. chil _____

2. sur _____   5. _____ ent   8. _____ e dy

3. _____ gram   6. hun _____   9. coun _____

4 **Using Sight Words.** Fill in each blank with one of the sight words
from this lesson. Use each word only once.

1. Is the _____ milk in the _____?

2. Priscilla chopped up an _____ and put it in the _____.

3. I love Italian _____. Pizza and _____ are my favorites.

5 **Distinguishing Between *r* and *l*.** Underline the syllable you hear.

1. brun — blun   4. crup — clup   7. grat — glat

2. grip — glip   5. prif — plif   8. fred — fled

3. frim — flim   6. brog — blog   9. crus — clus

Now write *r* or *l* in the blanks below to complete the syllable you hear.

1. b___ut   4. c___ick   7. g___ot

2. g___an   5. p___og   8. f___em

3. f___ub   6. b___ib   9. c___ad

6 **Word Building with Blends Containing *r* and *l*.** Write one of the *r*
or *l* blends below in each blank to form a word. Do not make the same
word twice.

bl   gl   fl   cl   pl   br   gr   fr   cr   pr   dr   tr

1. _____and   4. _____eam   7. _____ide   10. _____ock

2. _____and   5. _____ed   8. _____ight   11. _____ock

3. _____ain   6. _____ee   9. _____ight   12. _____ove

7 **The Possessive Apostrophe.** Rewrite the phrases below following these steps.

Step 1: Write the owner(s) or possessor(s).

    the president   the men
    the nurse   several cars

Step 2: Add an apostrophe.

    the president'   the men'
    the nurse'   several cars'

Step 3: Add an *s* if you can hear one when you say the phrase.

    the president's speech   the men's plans
    the nurse's duties   several cars' fenders

1. the address of the Brents   _____

2. the point of the story   _____

3. the uniforms of the players   _____

4. the sponsors of the programs   _____

5. the orders of the boss   _____

6. the parents of the children   _____

7. the crew of the ship   _____

8. the problems of Grace   _____

8 **Hearing Accent.** When words of more than one syllable are pronounced, usually one syllable receives more stress than the others. We call the syllable that receives the most stress the *accented* syllable. Dictionaries use an accent mark (') in the pronunciation guide to show which syllable is accented.

Listen to the words below, and place an accent mark on the accented syllable.

1. pro   gram   4. gal   lop   7. prof   it

2. num   ber   5. for   got   8. blan   ket

3. oc   cur   6. pro   pel   9. ben   e   fit

9 **Doubling Pattern 2.** In some words of more than one syllable, the final consonant is doubled before adding an ending that starts with a vowel. Study the pattern and follow the directions below.

Pattern: In words of two or more syllables, double the final consonant only when:
- the last syllable has one vowel and one final consonant
- the last syllable is the accented syllable
- and the ending starts with a vowel.

1. Look at each word below. Check the appropriate box if the last syllable has one vowel, one final consonant, and is accented. If you check all three boxes and the ending begins with a vowel, double the final consonant before adding the ending.

2. If you do not check all three boxes or the ending begins with a consonant, do not double the final consonant. Write the word on the line provided.

The Last Syllable:

	Has one vowel	One final consonant	Is accented		
1. control				+ ing	_____
2. transmit				+ ed	_____
3. propel				+ er	_____
4. prosper				+ ing	_____
5. blanket				+ ing	_____
6. begin				+ ing	_____

10 **Writing Sentences.** On the lines below, write the sentences that you hear.

1. _____

2. _____

3. _____

4. _____

5. _____

Lesson 4

The Blends *st*, *sp*, *sn*, *sl*, and *sm*

Blends

1 Listening

st

Listen to the sound of *st* in these words.

stack	stay	stick	stock
stain	stable	stiff	stuck
stake	steam	still	study
state	steel	stitch	stuff

sp

Listen to the sound of *sp* in these words.

spill	space	spice	inspect
spell	spade	Spain	respect
spend	speak	Spanish	special

sn

Listen to the sound of *sn* in these words.

snap	snail	snow
snack	snake	snore
sniff	sneak	sneeze

sl

Listen to the sound of *sl* in these words.

slap	sled	slick	sleep
slipper	slide	slice	sleeve

sm

Listen to the sound of *sm* in these words.

smell	smear	smile
small	smudge	smoke

2 **Writing Words.** On the lines below, write the words that you hear.

1. _____   5. _____   9. _____

2. _____   6. _____   10. _____

3. _____   7: _____   11. _____

4. _____   8. _____   12. _____

3 **Review of Doubling Patterns 1 and 2.** Add the endings and write the words on the lines provided.

Part A. These words all end with one vowel and one final consonant. For the two-syllable words, you must determine if the last syllable is accented before deciding whether or not to double the final consonant.

1. hit + er _____   6. clip + ing _____

2. control + er _____   7. drip + ing _____

3. forgot + en _____   8. slip + er _____

4. trim + ed _____   9. clot + ed _____

5. market + ing _____   10. admit + ance _____

Part B. Add the endings to these words. Double the final consonant when necessary.

1. repair + ed _____   6. forget + ing _____

2. refer + al _____   7. offer + ed _____

3. invent + ing _____   8. fluster + ed _____

4. commit + ee _____   9. prefer + ing _____

5. exert + ing _____   10. reject + ing _____

Part C. Choose two of the words you formed and use them in sentences.

1. _____

2. _____

④ Writing Words by Syllables. Write each word your teacher dictates by syllables. Then write the whole word on the line provided. Beside each syllable write the syllable type (C for closed, O for open, **Cle** for consonant plus *le*, **VC**e for vowel-consonant-*e*, or D for double vowel).

First Syllable	Second Syllable	Third Syllable	Fourth Syllable	Whole Word
1. _____	_____			_____
2. _____	_____			_____
3. _____	_____			_____
4. _____	_____			_____
5. _____	_____	_____		_____
6. _____	_____	_____		_____
7. _____	_____	_____	_____	_____
8. _____	_____	_____	_____	_____

⑤ The Possessive Form of Personal Pronouns. Pronouns have special forms that are used to show ownership or possession. These forms do not use an apostrophe, even though they may end in *s*. Study the examples below.

Singular Possessives		Plural Possessives
mine	his	ours
yours	hers	yours
	its	theirs

Write the sentences you hear.

1. _____ 5. _____

2. _____ 6. _____

3. _____ 7. _____

4. _____ 8. _____

6 **Homonyms:** *Its* **and** *It's*. Read the sentences below.

1. The kitten is chasing *its* tail.
2. You can't judge a book by *its* cover.
3. *It's* never too late.
4. It looks like *it's* going to rain.

Its is the possessive form of the pronoun *it*. Like other possessive pronouns, it does not need an apostrophe.

It's is the contraction for *it is*. Use the apostrophe only when you can substitute *it is* in the sentence.

Fill in either *its* or *it's* to complete the sentences below.

1. _____ snowing outside.

2. Please feed the dog _____ dinner.

3. The snake has shed _____ skin.

4. Do you know if _____ ten o'clock yet?

5. The spider caught a fly in _____ web.

6. If _____ not one thing, _____ another.

7 **Writing Sentences.** On the lines below, write the sentences that you hear.

1. _____

2. _____

3. _____

4. _____

5. _____

6. _____

7. _____

8. _____

Lesson 5

The Blends *sc*, *sk*, *sw*, and *tw*

┌─────────────────────────────────────┐
│   **Sight Words**   │
│   school   scene   science   │
│   schedule   scent   scissors   │
└─────────────────────────────────────┘

Blends

1 **Listening**

sc

Listen to the sound of *sc* in these words.

scab	scuff	score	scout
scar	scale	scare	scarlet
scum	scold	scarce	scatter

sk

Listen to the sound of *sk* in these words.

skin	skirt	skull	sky
skip	skating	skillet	skiing

sw

Listen to the sound of *sw* in these words.

swim	swell	Swiss	sweep
swam	swing	swear	sweet
swimming	switch	sweat	sweetheart

tw

Listen to the sound of *tw* in these words.

twin	twelve	twist	tweed
twice	twenty	twitch	between
twine	twenty-five	twinkle	twilight

2 **Writing Words.** On the lines below, write the words that you hear.

1. _____   4. _____   7. _____

2. _____   5. _____   8. _____

3. _____   6. _____   9. _____

3 **Word Building.** Write one of the blends below in each blank to form a word. Do not make the same word twice.

	sc	*sk*	*sw*	*tw*

1. _____am   5. _____eed   9. _____in

2. _____are   6. _____ice   10. _____in

3. _____ate   7. _____im   11. _____old

4. _____ear   8. _____im   12. _____um

4 **Dictionary Skills: Finding the Correct Spelling.** In this lesson, the sound /sk/ is spelled three different ways. It is spelled *sk* as in *skip* and *skate*, *sc* as in *scab* and *scale*, and *sch* as in *scholar* and *schedule*. A dictionary can help you find the correct spelling of the /sk/ sound in a given word.

Use a dictionary to find the correct spelling of the words spelled phonetically below. The most common spelling for /sk/ is *sc*, so look for that first. When you find the word that has the meaning given, write the correct spelling on the line provided. The first one has been done to get you started.

Phonetic Spelling	Meaning	Correct Spelling
1. /skĕp′tĭk/	someone who doubts	_Skeptic_
2. /skŭlp′tər/	an artist who works with stone or clay	_____
3. /skēm/	a plan or plot	_____
4. /skăl′pəl/	a small knife used by doctors	_____
5. /skĕl′ə tən/	the bony framework of the body	_____
6. /skăv′ in jər/	an animal that feeds on dead things	_____

Use two of these words in sentences.

1. _____

2. _____

5 **Words with *Two* in Their Meanings.** Many words that begin with the blend *tw* are related in some way to the number *two*. Explain how each of the words below is related to the number *two*.

1. twin _____

2. twice _____

3. twelve _____

Many compound words are built with *two*. Write the meanings of the words below on the lines provided. Use your dictionary if you need help.

1. two-edged _____

2. two-faced _____

3. twosome _____

4. two-way _____

6 **The Soft *c*.** When a *c* has the sound /s/, it is called a soft *c*. Look at the words below. Underline the soft *c* in each word. Then circle the letter that follows the soft *c*.

1. process   5. criticize   9. icy

2. necessary   6. citizen   10. juicy

3. excellent   7. society   11. bicycle

4. succeed   8. decision   12. cylinder

Fill in the blanks in the pattern below.

  Pattern: When *c* is followed by _____, _____, or _____, it has a soft /s/ sound.

7 **Spelling Sight Words.** Four of the sight words in this lesson have the /s/ sound spelled *sc*. Write them on the lines below.

1. _____   2. _____   3. _____   4. _____

Circle the letter that comes after the *c* in these words.

Why is the *sc* pronounced /s/? _____

8 **Homonyms:** *Principal* and *Principle*. Look up the homonyms *principal* and *principle* in the dictionary and write a definition for each word on the lines below.

principal _____

_____

principle _____

_____

Write either *principal(s)* or *principle(s)* in the blanks below.

1. There is a new _____ at the high school.

2. I will vote for the candidate with the highest _____.

3. Grace was studying the _____ parts of verbs.

4. He is one of the _____ reporters for the newspaper.

5. Sir Isaac Newton studied the _____ of gravity.

6. They discussed several basic _____ at the meeting.

9 **Writing Sentences.** On the lines below, write the sentences that you hear.

1. _____

2. _____

3. _____

4. _____

5. _____

_____

6. _____

_____

Review of Unit 1

Blends That Begin Syllables

1 **Word Building.** Add one of the blends listed below to each of the word families to make a word. Do not make the same word twice.

bl	pl	fr	sk	sp
cl	br	gr	sl	st
fl	cr	pr	sm	sw
gl	dr	tr	sn	tw

1. _____ad

2. _____ag

3. _____ag

4. _____aise

5. _____am

6. _____ane

7. _____eak

8. _____eet

9. _____eet

10. _____ick

11. _____iff

12. _____ile

13. _____ill

14. _____ill

15. _____ime

16. _____itch

17. _____ock

18. _____ow

19. _____oze

20. _____uff

21. _____unk

2 **Review of Doubling Patterns 1 and 2**

Part A. Add the endings and write the new words on the lines provided. Double the final consonant when necessary.

1. forbid + en _____

2. swim + er _____

3. admit + ance _____

4. stop + ing _____

5. commit + ee _____

6. commit + ment _____

7. tax + able _____

8. twist + ing _____

9. drug + ist _____

10. scarce + ly _____

11. spot + ed _____

12. begin + er _____

Part B. On the lines below, write the phrases that you hear.

1. _____ 4. _____

2. _____ 5. _____

3. _____ 6. _____

3 **The Possessive Apostrophe.** Rewrite the phrases below using an apostrophe to show ownership or possession.

1. the club of the boys   _____

2. the car of the Browns   _____

3. the responsibility of the country _____

4. the bicycle of Dennis   _____

5. the softness of the blanket   _____

6. the son of Triana   _____

7. the last glow of twilight   _____

8. the problem of the Brelands   _____

9. the rights of women   _____

10. the honor of the scout   _____

4 **Possessive Pronouns.** Fill in the blanks in the sentences below with the appropriate word.

1. The ice cream belongs to us. It is _____.

2. The truck belongs to them. It is _____.

3. Those gloves belong to her. They are _____.

4. That ring has lost _____ glitter.

5. That present belongs to you. It is _____.

6. The swing belongs to him. It is _____.

5 **Review of Syllable Types.** Write each syllable below on a line under the correct heading.

deem	fle	be	pock	gle
hap	tac	ci	o	tone
train	mote	cle	sime	ceal

Closed   **Open**   **Cle**

1. _____   1. _____   1. _____

2. _____   2. _____   2. _____

3. _____   3. _____   3. _____

VCe   **Double Vowel**

1. _____   1. _____

2. _____   2. _____

3. _____   3. _____

6 **Writing Words by Syllables.** Write each word your teacher dictates by syllables. Then write the whole word on the line provided.

First Syllable	Second Syllable	Third Syllable	Fourth Syllable	Whole Word
1.				
2.				
3.				
4.				
5.				
6.				
7.				
8.				

7 **Review of Homonyms.** Write a sentence using each of the homonyms below.

1. its _____

2. it's _____

3. principal _____

4. principle _____

8 **Alternative Spellings for /sk/.** Below are three ways to spell /sk/. On the lines under each heading, write words that use those letters to spell /sk/.

sc	sk	sch
1. _____	1. _____	1. _____
2. _____	2. _____	2. _____
3. _____	3. _____	3. _____
4. _____	4. _____	
5. _____		
6. _____		

9 **Writing Sentences.** Write the sentences that you hear.

1. _____

2. _____

3. _____

4. _____

5. _____

6. _____

7. _____

8. _____

10 **Composing Paragraphs.** On a separate sheet of paper, write a short paragraph of three or four sentences about each of these pictures. Use some of the words listed below in your paragraphs.

address	brave	fled	smell
afraid	clutch	glow	smoke
blare	fire truck	problem	speed
blaze	flames	scare	tragedy

children	glide	skate	sled
February	gloves	skid	slide
freeze	practice	skiing	snowball
frozen	scarf	skill	snowy

11 **Crossword Puzzle.** Use the clues below to complete this crossword puzzle. Most of the answers are representative words or sight words from Unit 1 or contain the Unit 1 blends.

Across

1. The second month
4. An odor or smell
7. Not scared
8. Cause to run out: Don't ___ the beans.
9. People who teach boxers
11. The opposite of opening
12. A small stream
13. The first meal of the day
14. Afire, blazing
15. To take out a braid
18. A doorway
19. To answer

Down

1. Peaches and apples are two types of ___.
2. An appliance that keeps food cold
3. Not asleep
5. Applaud
6. The time between sunset and full night
8. A supply kept on hand
10. A timetable; a list of times
12. What a baby is rocked in
13. Started
16. To block from entering
17. Not wet

Lesson 6

The Digraph *sh* and the Suffixes *-tion*, *-sion*, and *-cian*

Sight Words		
sure	ocean	cushion
sugar	suspicion	fashion

Digraph

① Listening

sh

Listen to the sound of *sh* in these words.

she	shoe	shady	wish
shall	should	shears	flesh
shacks	shoulder	shining	blush

Suffixes

-tion

Listen to the sound of *-tion* in these words.

action	addition	attention	donation
fiction	inflation	imagination	vacation
station	pollution	occupation	transportation

-sion

Listen to the sound of *-sion* in these words.

session	admission	expression	division
profession	permission	discussion	television

-cian

Listen to the sound of *-cian* in these words.

magician	beautician	musician	optician

② Writing Words. On the lines below, write the words that you hear.

1. _____   4. _____   7. _____

2. _____   5. _____   8. _____

3. _____   6. _____   9. _____

3 **Words That End in -tion.** The letters *tion* at the end of a word are pronounced /shən/. The most common way to spell /shən/ is *tion*. With the exception of *fashion* and *cushion*, /shən/ is not spelled *shion*. Listen to the following words and write the missing syllables.

1. va _____ tion

2. _____ di tion

3. so lu _____

4. _____ trac tion

5. trans la _____

6. _____ si tion

7. in _____ tion

8. nu _____ tion

9. con cen _____ tion

10. e _____ u a tion

4 **Word Building with -tion.** The suffix *-tion* is a very common suffix. It is often used to change verbs into nouns. Sometimes when *-tion* is added, the root word changes or some other letters are added, but you can usually hear the changes.

Example: concentrate + tion = concentration

Add *-tion* to these verbs. Pronounce the new word before you spell it. Use the dictionary to check your spellings. The first one has been done to get you started.

1. situate + tion   *situation*

2. designate + tion _____

3. create + tion _____

4. educate + tion _____

5. illustrate + tion _____

6. operate + tion _____

7. frustrate + tion _____

8. expire + tion _____

9. explain + tion _____

10. devote + tion _____

Use three of the new words in sentences.

1. _____

2. _____

3. _____

5 **Words That End in -sion.** The most common way to spell /shən/ at the end of a word is -tion. The next most likely way to spell the ending /shən/ is -sion. The suffix -sion can also be used to change verbs into nouns. Listen to the following words and write the missing syllables.

1. _____ fes sion   4. _____ pres sion   7. sup er _____ sion

2. re vi _____   5. re _____ sion   8. col _____ sion

3. pro _____ sion   6. pro ces _____   9. _____ mis sion

Use three of the words above in sentences.

1. _____

2. _____

3. _____

6 **Root Words.** Write the root word from which each of the words in Exercise 5 was built.

1. _____   4. _____   7. _____

2. _____   5. _____   8. _____

3. _____   6. _____   9. _____

7 **Word Building with the Suffix -cian.** The suffix -cian is usually added to words to indicate a person who does some skilled work. Add the suffix -cian to the root words below to make a word meaning a person who has skill in a particular area. Use the dictionary to check your spellings.

1. magic + cian   _____   4. politics + cian   _____

2. statistics + cian   _____   5. electric + cian   _____

3. pediatrics + cian   _____   6. mathematics + cian _____

Look at the root words above and fill in the blanks in the following pattern.

Pattern: Words that end in -cian often have roots that end in _____ or _____.

8 **Discovering a Pattern.** In the representative words in this lesson, the sound /sh/ is spelled four different ways: *sh*, *ti*, *si*, and *ci*. Think about the representative words you have studied and fill in the blanks in the pattern below.

Pattern: At the beginning or end of a word, /sh/ is usually spelled _____.

Syllables pronounced /shən/ can be spelled _____, _____, or

_____. The most common spelling of /shən/ is _____.

9 **Writing Words by Syllables.** Write each word your teacher dictates by syllables. Then write the whole word on the line provided.

First Syllable	Second Syllable	Third Syllable	Fourth Syllable	Whole Word
1. _____	_____			_____
2. _____	_____	_____		_____
3. _____	_____	_____		_____
4. _____	_____	_____		_____
5. _____	_____	_____		_____
6. _____	_____	_____	_____	_____
7. _____	_____	_____	_____	_____
8. _____	_____	_____	_____	_____
9. _____	_____	_____	_____	_____

10 **Writing Sentences.** On the lines below, write the sentences that you hear.

1. _____

2. _____

3. _____

4. _____

5. _____

Lesson 7

The Digraphs *ph* and *ch* and the Suffix *-ture*

> **Sight Words**
>
> | | | |
> |---|---|---|
> | psychology | natural | chef |
> | psychologist | spatula | machine |

Digraphs

1 Listening

ph

Listen to the sound of *ph* in these words.

phone	physical	alphabet
phony	physician	telephone
phobia	photograph	microphone

ch
as /ch/

Listen to the sound of *ch* in these words.

check	chain	reach	rich
child	cheap	bleach	speech
chance	cheese	teacher	merchant

ch
as /k/

Listen to the sound of *ch* in these words.

chemical	chorus	ache
character	technical	anchor
Christmas	technician	stomach

Suffix
-ture

Listen to the sound of *-ture* in these words.

feature	nature	adventure	lecture
fracture	picture	agriculture	mixture

2 Writing Words. On the lines below, write the words that you hear.

1. _____   4. _____   7. _____

2. _____   5. _____   8. _____

3. _____   6. _____   9. _____

3 **Dictionary Skills: Word Origins.** Words have come into English from many different languages. Sometimes knowing what language a word comes from will help you remember how to spell it. Many dictionaries list the origins of root words. Look up the words below and write the language from which each came on the line beside it.

1. character _____

2. stomach _____

3. technology _____

4. chef _____

5. brochure _____

6. chauvinism _____

Now fill in the blanks in this pattern.

Ch often spells /k/ in words taken from _____.

Ch often spells /sh/ in words taken from _____.

4 **The Roots *psych-* and *psycho-***

1. Write the words that you hear.

_____   _____

What language do these words probably come from? _____

How do you know? _____

2. Look up the root *psych-* or *psycho-* and write the meaning on the line below.

_____

3. Write two other words that have *psych-* or *psycho-* as a root.

_____   _____

4. Use one of these words in a sentence.

_____

_____

5 **Word Building: Alternative Spellings for /chur/.** The most common way to spell /chur/ at the end of a word is *ture*. However, when *-er* is added to a word that ends in *ch*, then /chur/ is spelled *cher*. Fill in the blanks in the sentences below with *ture* or *cher*. Use your dictionary, if necessary.

1. The sick child had a very high tempera___ ___ ___ ___.

2. Do you ever wish you could know what the fu___ ___ ___ ___ will bring?

3. Our softball team needs a new pit___ ___ ___ ___ and a new cat___ ___ ___ ___.

4. The company Chuck works for has begun to manufac___ ___ ___ ___ blea___ ___ ___ ___s.

5. The legisla___ ___ ___ ___ passed the bill and sent it to the governor for his signa___ ___ ___ ___.

6 **The Possessive Apostrophe.** Rewrite the phrases below using an apostrophe to show ownership or possession.

1. the beauty of nature _____

2. the features of the twins _____

3. the office of the physician _____

4. the room of the teachers _____

5. the temperature of the child _____

6. the adventure of the scouts _____

7 **Writing Sentences.** On the lines below, write the sentences that you hear.

1. _____

2. _____

3. _____

4. _____

5. _____

8 **Puzzle.** Match the clues below with words from the list at the right. Use the words to fill in the blocks of the puzzle. When you have filled in all the correct answers, the shaded blocks will spell a new word ending in *-ture*. The first one has been done to get you started.

Clues

1. a group of lawmakers
2. something created or made up
3. to use machinery to make something
4. an exciting or difficult experience
5. a speech given to teach or inform
6. a desire to succeed or achieve something
7. a photograph or drawing of something
8. the exchange of ideas and opinions
9. a doctor who treats children
10. to break or crack

Word List

adventure
ambition
discussion
fracture
invention
lecture
√ legislature
manufacture
pediatrician
picture

1. L E G I S L A T U R E

2. ☐☐☐☐☐☐☐☐

3. ☐☐☐☐☐☐☐☐☐

4. ☐☐☐☐☐☐☐☐

5. ☐☐☐☐☐☐

6. ☐☐☐☐☐☐☐☐

7. ☐☐☐☐☐☐

8. ☐☐☐☐☐☐☐☐☐

9. ☐☐☐☐☐☐☐☐☐☐

10. ☐☐☐☐☐☐☐

Write the new word ending in *-ture*: _____

Use this new word in a sentence. Use your dictionary if you need to.

_____

_____

Lesson 8

The Digraphs *th* and *wh*

Sight Words		
thought	whose	wear
Thomas	whoever	weather

Digraphs

1 Listening

th
as /th/

Listen to the sound of *th* in these words.

thick	thank	both	tooth
thirsty	think	bath	truth
thunder	thirteen	athletic	anything

th
as /th/

Listen to the sound of *th* in these words.

than	there	thus	smooth
that	their	these	brother
this	themselves	though	together

wh

Listen to the sound of *wh* in these words.

why	where	whip	whether
when	which	wheel	whistle
what	whichever	white	awhile

2 Writing Words. On the lines below, write the words that you hear.

1. _____   4. _____   7. _____

2. _____   5. _____   8. _____

3. _____   6. _____   9. _____

3 **Words That Sound Almost Alike.** Underline the word that you hear in each pair.

1. weather — whether   2. wear — where

These pairs of words sound almost alike, but their meanings are very different. Fill in the correct word to complete each sentence below.

1. Thomas doesn't like to _____ a necktie.

2. Let me know _____ or not you can come to dinner.

3. Do you remember _____ you put the picture frames?

4. I hope the _____ is fine for your picnic tomorrow.

4 **Numbers That End in _th_.** Numbers that end in _th_ are used to indicate the position of something in a series. Sometimes the spelling of the root number changes when _th_ is added. When the root number ends in _ty_, the _y_ is changed to _i_ and _eth_ is added. Spell the numbers ending in _th_ below. Use your dictionary if you are not sure of a spelling.

1. 4th _____   5. 12th _____

2. 5th _____   6. 30th _____

3. 8th _____   7. 40th _____

4. 9th _____   8. 90th _____

5 **Using the Apostrophe to Form Plurals.** Add _'s_ to form the plurals of letters used as words and of abbreviations with periods. Study the examples below. Then write the sentences that you hear.

p's and q's   x's and o's   lb.'s   jr.'s   V.I.P.'s   I.Q.'s

1. _____

2. _____

3. _____

4. _____

5. _____

6 **Review of Contractions.** When we put two words together and leave out one or more letters, we have a contraction. We put an apostrophe in place of the letter or letters we leave out. Study the example and then form the contractions below.

Example: are + not = aren't

1. we + are _____

2. is + not _____

3. have + not _____

4. should + not _____

5. he + will _____

6. it + is _____

7. will + not _____

8. I + am _____

9. could + have _____

10. they + are _____

7 **Homonyms: *Their*, *There*, and *They're***

Their is a possessive pronoun. It is used to indicate *something that belongs to them*.

There means *in that place*. It answers the question *where* and contains the word *here*.

They're is the contraction for *they are*. Use it only when you can substitute *they are* in the sentence.

Study the example sentences and then fill in the correct word to complete each of the sentences below.

Examples: This is *their* house.   *Their* car is red.
          Put the box *there*.   *There* were six letters in the mail.
          They're all going with us.   Do you know when *they're* coming?

1. _____ cat is in the tree.

2. _____ going to the party, aren't they?

3. I am going over _____ after school.

4. It's _____ decision.

5. _____ isn't any reason to be upset.

6. _____ going to have twins.

8 **Writing a Letter.** Write a letter to a friend telling about something that has happened to you recently or something you are planning to do soon. Begin with the date in the upper right corner. Use at least five words that contain *th* or *wh*.

_____

Dear _____,

_____

_____

_____

_____

_____

_____

_____

_____

_____

_____

Sincerely,

_____

9 **Writing Sentences.** On the lines below, write the sentences that you hear.

1. _____

2. _____

3. _____

4. _____

5. _____

Review of Unit 2

Digraphs and Suffixes

1 **Words That End in /shən/.** Write three of the ways to spell /shən/ at the end of words.

_____   _____   _____

Fill in the correct spelling of /shən/ to complete each of the words below.

1. ambi _____
2. admis_____
3. infla_____
4. opti _____

5. ses _____
6. sta _____
7. vaca _____
8. dona_____

9. magi _____
10. transporta_____
11. conversa _____
12. occupa _____

What is the most common way to spell /shən/ at the end of a word? _____

What is the ending that indicates a person skilled in some work? _____

Write two sight words that end in _shion_.

_____   _____

2 **Words That End in /chur/.** Write the words that you hear.

1._____
2._____

3._____
4._____

5._____
6._____

How is the sound /chur/ usually spelled at the end of words? _____

3 **Homonyms.** Use each of these homonyms correctly in a sentence.

1. their _____
2. there _____
3. they're _____

4 **Review of the Apostrophe.** Rewrite the phrases and sentences below filling in the missing apostrophes.

1. Jims transfer _____

2. Mind your ps and qs. _____

3. the childrens father _____

4. Its not necessary. _____

5. Theyre all musicians. _____

6. Youve got my permission. _____

5 **Finding Root Words.** Write the root word for each of the words below. Use the dictionary to check your spelling if necessary.

1. admission _____ 7. communication _____

2. celebration _____ 8. confusion _____

3. confession _____ 9. imagination _____

4. combination _____ 10. electrician _____

5. beautician _____ 11. suspension _____

6. occupation _____ 12. satisfaction _____

6 **Writing Sentences.** Write the sentences that you hear.

1. _____

_____

2. _____

3. _____

4. _____

5. _____

6. _____

7 **Composing Sentences.** On the lines provided, write one or two sentences about each of these pictures.

_____

_____

_____

_____

_____

_____

_____

_____

_____

8 **Crossword Puzzle.** Use the clues below to complete this crossword puzzle. Most of the answers are representative words or sight words from Unit 2 or contain Unit 2 digraphs or endings.

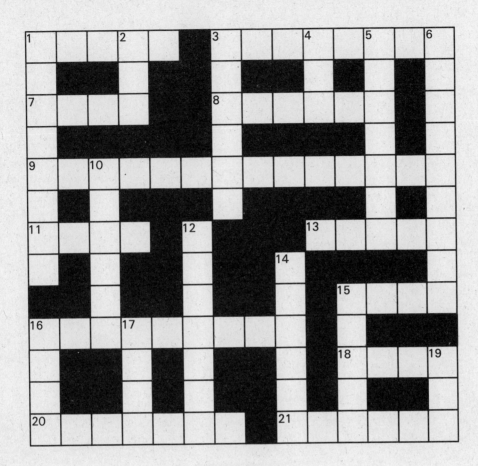

Across

1. The opposite of stale
3. The ABC's
7. Pain
8. A need for water
9. A system of traveling
11. The opposite of poor
13. What a magician performs
15. The opposite of ill
16. December 25
18. Leave out
20. A characteristic or quality
21. Large scissors

Down

1. To break, as a bone
2. The opposite of he
3. A movement, act, or deed
4. The opposite of his: ___ book
5. Taking a bath
6. Related to mechanical or industrial skills
10. This holds a boat in place.
12. Almost a homonym of weather
14. Wants or desires: He ___ he could go with us.
15. Complete; entire
16. A French cook
17. The contraction for *is not*
19. A contraction for *it is*: "My Country ___ of Thee"

Lesson 9

The Blends *str*, *scr*, *spl*, and *spr*

Blends

1 **Listening**

str   Listen to the sound of *str* in these words.

strap	strike	stream
string	struck	street
strong	stretch	strange

scr   Listen to the sound of *scr* in these words.

scrap	scrape	describe
scrub	scream	description
scratch	screen	inscription

spl   Listen to the sound of *spl* in these words.

split	splice	splatter
splash	splinter	splendid

spr   Listen to the sound of *spr* in these words.

spray	spring	spry
sprain	sprinkle	spree

2 **Writing Words.** On the lines below, write the words that you hear.

1. _____   5. _____   9. _____

2. _____   6. _____   10. _____

3. _____   7. _____   11. _____

4. _____   8. _____   12. _____

3 **Word Building.** Listen to the dictated words and fill in the missing syllable to complete each word below.

1. _____ ture   5. pre scrip _____

2. _____ ble   6. _____ e gy

3. splut _____   7. un _____ pu lous

4. _____ dor   8. in de _____ ti ble

Use two of these words in sentences. Look up the words in your dictionary if you need to.

1. _____

_____

2. _____

_____

4 **Review of Doubling Pattern 2.** Review the pattern and follow the directions below.

Pattern: In words of two or more syllables, double the final consonant only when:
- the last syllable has one vowel and one final consonant
- the last syllable is the accented syllable
- and the ending starts with a vowel.

Add the endings to the words below. Double the final consonant when necessary.

1. admit + ing _____   7. splatter + ed _____

2. splinter + ing _____   8. begin + ing _____

3. propel + er _____   9. forget + ing _____

4. omit + ing _____   10. splendid + ly _____

5. inspect + or _____   11. transmit + er _____

6. forbid + en _____   12. prosper + ous _____

5 **Reviewing Patterns for Adding Endings.** Review these patterns for adding endings.

1. **Doubling Pattern 1.** Double the final consonant if the word has one syllable, one vowel, and one final consonant, and the ending begins with a vowel. Do not double *w* or *x*.

2. **Doubling Pattern 2.** In words of more than one syllable, the final consonant is doubled if the last syllable is accented and has one vowel and one final consonant, and if the ending starts with a vowel.

3. **Silent *e* Pattern 1.** Drop the final silent *e* if the ending begins with a vowel.

4. **The Ending -*es*.** When a word ends in *s*, *x*, *z*, *ch*, or *sh*, add -*es* instead of -*s*.

5. **Changing *y* to *i*.** When adding an ending to a word that ends in C*y*, change the *y* to *i* unless the ending begins with *i*. Add -*es* instead of -*s* to nouns and verbs.

6. **Changing *f* to *v*.** The plural of some words which end in *f* or *fe* is formed by changing the *f* or *fe* to *v* and adding -*es*.

Write the root word for each of the words listed below. Then write the number of the pattern which was followed when the ending was added. The first one has been done to get you started.

	Root Word	Pattern
1. scrubbed	scrub	1
2. describing		
3. propeller		
4. shadier		
5. stretches		
6. shelves		
7. stranger		
8. splitting		
9. glasses		
10. forgotten		

6 **Words That End in -fer.** When Doubling Pattern 2 is used with words that end in -fer, it is more difficult to decide whether or not to double the final r. This is because the accent sometimes changes to a different syllable when the ending is added.

Part A. Pronounce the words below and mark the accented syllable with an accent mark (').

1. re fer   re fer ral   ref er ence

2. con fer   con fer ring   con fer ence

Underline the words in which the r was doubled and fill in the blanks below.

1. The r is doubled if the accent stays on the _____ syllable when the ending is added.

2. The r is not doubled if the accent shifts to the _____ syllable when the ending is added.

Part B. Add the endings to the words below. Remember to pronounce the word with the ending added to determine which syllable is accented. Use the dictionary if necessary.

1. prefer + ed _____   6. infer + ing _____

2. prefer + able _____   7. infer + ence _____

3. prefer + ence _____   8. differ + ence _____

4. prefer + ing _____   9. differ + ed _____

5. offer + ed _____   10. refer + ee _____

7 **Writing Sentences.** On the lines below, write the sentences that you hear.

1. _____

2. _____

3. _____

4. _____

5. _____

Lesson 10

The Blends *squ*, *shr*, and *thr*

Sight Words			
squirrel	shriek	shrewd	thread

Blends

1 Listening

squ

Listen to the sound of *squ* in these words.

square	squad	squeeze
squeak	squat	squander
squeal	squall	squeamish

shr

Listen to the sound of *shr* in these words.

shred	shrink	shrimp
shrub	shrank	shrine
shrill	shrunk	shrivel

thr

Listen to the sound of *thr* in these words.

thrill	throw	three
throng	threw	thrive
thrust	through	throat

2 Writing Words. On the lines below, write the words that you hear.

1. _____   4. _____   7. _____

2. _____   5. _____   8. _____

3. _____   6. _____   9. _____

3 **Dictionary Skills: Guide Words.** Below are pairs of guide words that might be found on dictionary pages. Decide if the words listed below each pair would appear on the dictionary page that has those guide words. Underline each word that would be found on that page.

1. **square — squeal**

   squad   squash   squeak   squall

2. **shred — shrink**

   shrill   shrank   shrimp   shrewd

3. **three — thrive**

   thread   threw   thrill   threat

4. **squander — squeeze**

   squeamish   squirrel   squadron   squat

5. **shrivel — shrunk**

   shriek   shrub   shrug   shrive

6. **throw — thrust**

   through   throat   throng   thrush

4 **Writing Words by Syllables.** Write each word your teacher dictates by syllables. Then write the whole word on the line provided.

First Syllable	Second Syllable	Third Syllable	Fourth Syllable	Whole Word
1. _____	_____			_____
2. _____	_____			_____
3. _____	_____			_____
4. _____	_____	_____		_____
5. _____	_____	_____		_____
6. _____	_____	_____	_____	_____
7. _____	_____	_____	_____	_____
8. _____	_____	_____	_____	_____

Use two of the words above in sentences.

1. _____

2. _____

5 **Homonyms:** *Threw* **and** *Through*. *Threw* is the past tense of *throw*. Study the examples below to see several ways that *through* is used.

1. We wandered *through* the shopping mall.   3. Are you *through* with that assignment?
2. It rained all *through* the afternoon.   4. He *threw* the ball *through* the window.

Use each of these homonyms in a sentence of your own.

threw   _____

   _____

through   _____

   _____

6 **Review of Changing *y* to *i*.** When adding an ending to a word that ends in a consonant plus *y*, change the *y* to *i* unless the ending begins with *i*. Add *-es* instead of *-s* to nouns and verbs.

Part A. Add the endings to these words.

1. sky + es   _____   7. cry + ing   _____

2. crazy + ly   _____   8. thirsty + er   _____

3. squeaky + est _____   9. technology + es _____

4. library + es   _____   10. pretty + est   _____

5. thirty + eth   _____   11. study + ing   _____

6. century + es _____   12. tragedy + es   _____

Part B. Write the phrases you hear.

1. _____   6. _____

2. _____   7. _____

3. _____   8. _____

4. _____   9. _____

5. _____   10. _____

7 Writing Sentences. On the lines below, write the sentences that you hear.

1. _____

2. _____

3. _____

4. _____

5. _____

8 Puzzle. Use the clues at the left to fill in the blocks of the puzzle. Refer to the list of answer words at the bottom of the page if you need to. When all the correct answers are filled in, the shaded blocks will spell a new word that begins with a blend.

Clues

1. used with a needle for sewing

2. to make smaller

3. a small tree-climbing rodent

4. to press firmly; to hug

5. a rectangle with four equal sides

6. a small, edible shellfish

7. to hurl or fling through the air

8. to shrink and wrinkle

9. a team of people

The new word: _____

Write a sentence using the new word.

_____

Word List: shrimp   shrivel   square   squirrel   throw
shrink   squad   squeeze   thread

Review of Unit 3

Beginning Blends of Three Letters

1 **Word Building.** Add one of the beginning blends below to each word family to make a word. Do not make the same word twice.

str   scr   spl   spr   squ   shr   thr

1. _____ap
2. _____ay
3. _____ay
4. _____eak
5. _____eam

6. _____eam
7. _____ed
8. _____eeze
9. _____ice
10. _____ike

11. _____ill
12. _____ill
13. _____ing
14. _____ong
15. _____ub

2 **Adding Endings.** Add the endings to the words below following the patterns you have studied.

1. split + ing _____
2. thirsty + er _____
3. inspect + or _____
4. thrive + ing _____
5. shelf + s *or* es _____
6. shop + ing _____
7. scrub + er _____
8. refer + ed _____
9. fifty + eth _____
10. permit + ing _____

11. reply + s *or* es _____
12. scatter + ing _____
13. squat + er _____
14. bleach + s *or* es _____
15. fly + ing _____
16. scratch + s *or* es _____
17. strike + ing _____
18. commit + ee _____
19. lecture + ing _____
20. century + s *or* es _____

3 **Using Words with Many Syllables.** Fill in the blanks in the sentences with the words listed below. Use each word only once.

concentration   conversation   expression   responsible
congratulate   especially   illustrations   spectacular
Constitution   explanation   nutrition   substitute

1. Good health depends on good _____.

2. I want to _____ you on your success.

3. Did Steve give you an _____ for his absence?

4. The Fourth of July fireworks were _____.

5. The three men were having a very lively _____.

6. Shirley is not _____ fond of that type of music.

7. Do you know who was _____ for the accident?

8. If you can't attend the meeting, will you send a _____?

9. The speaker gave several _____ to explain his point of view.

10. The subject Clint is studying requires a great deal of _____.

11. The Supreme Court interprets the _____ of the United States.

12. You should have seen the _____ on Chris's face when we walked in.

4 **Composing Sentences.** Choose three of the words listed in Exercise 3 and use them in sentences of your own.

1. _____

_____

2. _____

_____

3. _____

_____

5 **Composing a Paragraph**. On a separate sheet of paper, write a paragraph of three or four sentences about this scene. Use some of the words listed below in your sentences.

scream	sprain	stretch	throat
shriek	squad	threw	throng
shrill	strength	thrill	throw

6 **Writing Sentences**. On the lines below, write the sentences that you hear.

1. _____

2. _____

3. _____

4. _____

5. _____

6. _____

7 **Crossword Puzzle.** Use the clues below to complete this crossword puzzle. Most of the answers are representative words or sight words from Unit 3 or contain Unit 3 blends.

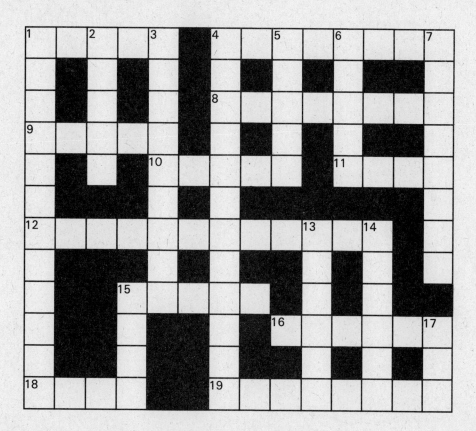

Across

1. A small plant or bush
4. To tell about
8. The opposite of crooked
9. To kneel with your weight on your heels; to crouch
10. A small piece of cloth; something left over
11. Twelve months
12. Words written or engraved on monuments
15. A favorite ice cream dish: banana ___
16. The opposite of outside
18. Snoopy; not minding your own business
19. Force or power: He has great ___.

Down

1. An order for a magazine
2. A TV program the second time it is shown
3. A strip of leather for fastening a boot
4. Words that describe
5. A thin strip used for fastening something
6. Wet weather: It was very ___.
7. To place on a throne
13. The second color in the rainbow
14. Thin cord used for tying packages
15. Quick; able to move easily
17. An ending for numbers that indicates position in a series

Lesson 11

The Blends *nd*, *nt*, *nce*, and *nse*

```
                    Sight Words
        guard      view       interview
        guardian   review     restaurant
```

Blends

1 Listening

nd

Listen to the sound of *nd* in these words.

bind	bandage	defend	fond
find	handful	offend	found
remind	grandfather	pretend	respond

nt

Listen to the sound of *nt* in these words.

pint	aunt	cent	rent
faint	infant	sent	payment
complaint	important	spent	argument

nce

Listen to the sound of *nce* in these words.

dance	fence	once	since
chance	absence	ounce	convince
entrance	sentence	announce	experience
insurance	residence	pronounce	difference

nse

Listen to the sound of *nse* in these words.

rinse	defense	expense	sense
tense	offense	response	license

2 Writing Words. On the lines below, write the words that you hear.

1. _____   4. _____   7. _____

2. _____   5. _____   8. _____

3. _____   6. _____   9. _____

3 **Distinguishing Between** *nd* **and** *nt*. Underline the word that you hear in each pair below.

1. bend — bent   4. send — sent   7. grand — grant

2. pend — pent   5. tend — tent   8. spend — spent

3. rend — rent   6. planned — plant   9. found — fount

4 **Word Building: Alternative Spellings for** /ns/. Words that end in the sound /ns/ can be spelled *nce*, *nse*, or *nts*, although *nce* is much more common than *nse*. Fill in the blanks in the sentences below with *nce*, *nse*, or *nts*. Use your dictionary if you need to check the spelling of any words.

1. When my car broke down, a stranger stopped and offered assista___ ___ ___.

2. Clint gained a lot of confide___ ___ ___ from his public speaking course.

3. Kent will be marching in the Independe___ ___ ___ Day parade.

4. The boss will cover our expe___ ___ ___s for the confere___ ___ ___.

5. My grandmother always says "Sile___ ___ ___ is golden."

6. The story Grant read to the kids was all about gia___ ___ ___.

7. Brian has to renew his driver's lice___ ___ ___ next month.

8. Our coach always used to say "The best offe___ ___ ___ is a good defe___ ___ ___."

5 **Word Building with** *-ance* **and** *-ence*. The suffixes *-ance* and *-ence* can be used to form nouns from verbs. Form the nouns indicated below. Remember to follow the patterns that you have studied for adding endings.

1. admit + ance _____   6. differ + ence _____

2. insure + ance _____   7. occur + ence _____

3. attend + ance _____   8. reside + ence _____

4. ignore + ance _____   9. prefer + ence _____

5. apply + ance _____   10. interfere + ence _____

6 **Review of Silent *e* Pattern 1**. The silent *e* at the end of a word is dropped when an ending starting with a vowel is added. Add the endings to the words below.

1. strike + ing _____   5. rinse + ing _____

2. dance + ed _____   6. brave + ly _____

3. square + ly _____   7. strange + er _____

4. license + ed _____   8. entrance + ing _____

7 **Silent *e* Pattern 2**. Answer the questions below to discover another silent *e* pattern.

Part A: Write the words that you hear and answer the questions.

1. _____   2. _____   3. _____

Do these words have a hard or soft *c*? _____

What letters give the *c*'s that sound? _____

Part B: Write the words that you hear and answer the questions.

1. _____   2. _____   3. _____

Do these words have a hard or soft *c*? _____

What letter gives the *c*'s that sound? _____

Part C: Look at the words below and answer the questions.

trace + ed = traced   trace + ing = tracing   trace + able = traceable

When *-ed* and *-ing* are added to *trace*, is the final *e* kept or dropped? _____

When *-able* is added to *trace*, is the final *e* kept or dropped? _____

What sound would the *c* have if the silent *e* in *traceable* were dropped? _____

Pattern: When an ending that begins with *a* is added to a word that ends in *ce*, the silent *e* is kept to retain the soft *c* sound.

8 **Adding Endings to Words That End in _ce_.** Add the endings to the words below following Silent _e_ Pattern 2.

1. dance + ing _____

2. pronounce + ed _____

3. pronounce + able _____

4. peace + able _____

5. convince + ing _____

6. embrace + ing _____

7. embrace + able _____

8. notice + ed _____

9. notice + able _____

10. announce + er _____

9 **Word Building.** Add the prefixes and suffixes to the root words following the patterns you have studied.

1. in + expense + ive _____

2. per + form + ance _____

3. in + offense + ive _____

4. en + force + able _____

5. in + convenient + ly _____

6. in + defense + ible _____

7. un + convince + ing _____

8. dis + appear + ance _____

Use three of these words in sentences.

1. _____

2. _____

3. _____

10 **Writing Sentences.** On the lines below, write the sentences that you hear.

1. _____

2. _____

3. _____

4. _____

5. _____

6. _____

Lesson 12

The Blends *ng*, *nk*, *nch*, and *nge*

```
                    Sight Words
        England      finger      longer
        English      linger      younger
```

Blends

① Listening

ng   Listen to the sound of *ng* in these words.

ring	young	longing	tongue
rang	wrong	nothing	hanger
rung	strongly	standing	singer

nk   Listen to the sound of *nk* in these words.

ink	sink	shrank
bank	sank	crankcase
trunk	sunken	thankful

nch   Listen to the sound of *nch* in these words.

bunch	ranch	inch	French
lunch	branch	pinch	wrench
munch	brunch	clinch	workbench

nge   Listen to the sound of *nge* in these words.

hinge	orange	exchange	lunge
cringe	changeable	strangely	lounge
fringe	arrangement	angelfish	challenge

2 **Writing Words.** On the lines below, write the words that you hear.

1. _____   5. _____   9. _____

2. _____   6. _____   10. _____

3. _____   7. _____   11. _____

4. _____   8. _____   12. _____

3 **Distinguishing Between *ng* and *nk*.** Underline the word that you hear in each pair below.

1. brink — bring   4. hunk — hung   7. hank — hang

2. think — thing   5. rink — ring   8. sinking — singing

3. stink — sting   6. bank — bang   9. winking — winging

4 **Word Building: Compound Words.** Build the compound words below. All of these compounds are closed.

1. song + bird _____   10. lunch + room _____

2. bench + mark _____   11. long + hand _____

3. ring + side _____   12. inch + worm _____

4. cow + puncher _____   13. sink + hole _____

5. French + man _____   14. paper + hanger _____

6. ginger + bread _____   15. ranch + men _____

7. gold + finch _____   16. short + change _____

8. bank + book _____   17. shoe + string _____

9. key + punch _____   18. work + bench _____

Use two of these words in sentences.

1. _____

2. _____

5 Silent *e* Pattern 2

Part A. When a *g* has the sound /g/, it is called a hard *g*. Underline the hard
   g's in the words below.

1. again   2. sugar   3. foregone   4. goodness

What letters follow the *g*'s to give them a hard sound? _____

Part B. When a *g* has the sound /j/, it is called a soft *g*. Words that end in
   ge have the soft *g* sound. Underline the soft *g*'s in the words below.

1. charge   2. strange   3. challenge   4. engage

Part C. Study the words below and answer the questions which follow.

   1. change + ing = changing   change + able = changeable
   2. outrage + ed = outraged   outrage + ous = outrageous

When -*ed* and -*ing* are added to *change* and *outrage*, the final *e* is _____ .

When -*able* and -*ous* are added to *change* and *outrage*, the final *e* is _____ .

What sound would the *g* have in *changeable* and *outrageous* if the silent *e* were dropped?

_____

   Pattern: When an ending that begins with *a* or *o* is added to a word
      that ends in *ce* or *ge*, the silent *e* is kept to retain the soft *c*
      and *g* sounds.

6 Adding Endings to Words That End in *ge*. Add the endings to the
   words below. Remember to keep the silent *e* when necessary.

1. hinge + ing   _____   6. challenge + ing   _____

2. plunge + ers   _____   7. strange + er   _____

3. orange + ade   _____   8. advantage + ous   _____

4. revenge + ful   _____   9. outrage + ous + ly   _____

5. exchange + ing   _____   10. courage + ous + ly   _____

7 **Puzzle.** Use the clues at the left to fill in the blocks of the puzzle. All of the answers are representative words in this lesson. When all the correct answers are filled in, the shaded blocks will spell a new word that ends in *nge*.

Clues

1. to shrink or cower in fear

2. a limb of a tree

3. not anything

4. language spoken in France

5. what is worn on a finger

6. twelfth part of a foot

7. able to be altered

8. a warm cover in bed

9. chew with a crunching noise

10. not right

11. to ask for a contest or duel

The new *nge* word: _____

Now write a sentence using the new word.

_____

8 **Writing Sentences.** On the lines below, write the sentences that you hear.

1. _____

2. _____

3. _____

4. _____

5. _____

Review of Unit 4

Blends with *n* That End Syllables

1 **Word Building.** Write one of the ending blends below in each blank to make a word.

nd   nt   nce   nse   nch   nge   ng   nk

1. ba _____   7. fli _____   13. ru _____

2. bu _____   8. hi _____   14. se _____

3. cha _____   9. le _____   15. shri _____

4. cru _____   10. li _____   16. sti _____

5. de _____   11. pla _____   17. stra _____

6. dra _____   12. pri _____   18. wi _____

2 **Word Building.** Write the missing syllable of each word you hear.

1. _____ ment   4. _____ ket   7. of _____

2. pre _____   5. con _____   8. _____ ing

3. pro _____   6. com _____   9. res i _____

3 **Alternative Spellings for /ns/.** Write the phrases that you hear.

1. _____   6. _____

2. _____   7. _____

3. _____   8. _____

4. _____   9. _____

5. _____   10. _____

4 **Review of Silent *e* Patterns 1 and 2.** Add the endings to the words below.

1. dance + ing _____
2. plunge + ers _____
3. peace + able _____
4. hinge + ed _____
5. defense + ive _____
6. slice + ing _____
7. service + ing _____
8. service + able _____
9. bruise + ed _____
10. revenge + ful _____

11. embrace + able _____
12. notice + able _____
13. change + over _____
14. sense + ible _____
15. pronounce + able _____
16. advantage + ous _____
17. challenge + er _____
18. exchange + ing _____
19. courage + ous _____
20. dis + courage + ing _____

5 **Writing Words by Syllables.** Write each word your teacher dictates by syllables. Then write the whole word on the line provided.

First Syllable	Second Syllable	Third Syllable	Fourth Syllable	Whole Word
1. _____	_____	_____		_____
2. _____	_____	_____		_____
3. _____	_____	_____		_____
4. _____	_____	_____	_____	_____
5. _____	_____	_____	_____	_____
6. _____	_____	_____	_____	_____

Use one of these words in a sentence.

_____

6 **Writing Sentences.** On the lines below, write the sentences that you hear.

1. _____

   _____

2. _____

3. _____

4. _____

5. _____

6. _____

7. _____

   _____

7 **Composing a Paragraph.** On a separate sheet of paper, write a paragraph of at least three or four sentences about the scene below. Use some of the representative words from Unit 4 in your sentences.

8 **Crossword Puzzle.** Use the clues below to complete this crossword puzzle. Most of the answers are representative words or sight words from Unit 4 or contain the Unit 4 blends.

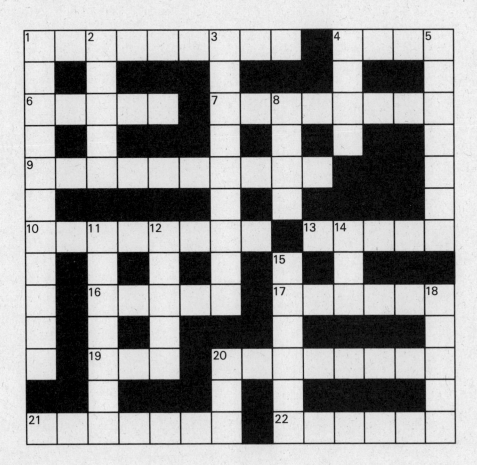

Across

1. A meeting between two people: a job ___
4. The opposite of go
6. Not relaxed
7. Powerfully or forcefully
9. A place to eat
10. Touching with the hands
13. To give or bestow: to ___ a wish
16. A trace of color
17. Heavenly beings
19. A possessive pronoun
20. An opening or doorway
21. London is its capital.
22. To protect against invaders

Down

1. To substitute for something else
2. Canvas houses
3. Protection against loss or injury
4. Fell to the bottom of the ocean
5. A sum of money paid
8. Monthly payment for an apartment
11. Not anything
12. Lets someone borrow
14. A carpet
15. Desired
18. The opposite of save
20. The opposite of beginning

Lesson 13

The Blends *mp*, *sp*, *st*, and *sk*

Sight Words		
hoist	personal	work
moist	personnel	clerk

Blends

1 **Listening**

mp

Listen to the sound of *mp* in these words.

damp	empty	bump	company
camping	impish	pumpkin	slumping

sp

Listen to the sound of *sp* in these words.

lisp	gasp	clasp
crisp	wasp	grasp

st

Listen to the sound of *st* in these words.

fast	cost	first	mostly
past	crust	assist	dentist

sk

Listen to the sound of *sk* in these words.

ask	desk	dusk	brisk
mask	disk	basketball	risking

2 **Writing Words.** On the lines below, write the words that you hear.

1. _____
2. _____
3. _____
4. _____
5. _____
6. _____
7. _____
8. _____
9. _____

3 **Sight Words: *Personal* and *Personnel*.** The words *personal* and *personnel* are often confused. Look up both words in your dictionary and write a definition for each word below.

personal _____

personnel _____

Use each word in a sentence of your own.

personal _____

personnel _____

4 **Distinguishing Between *sk* and *st*.** Underline the word that you hear in each pair below.

1. mask — mast   4. musk — must

2. dusk — dust   5. cask — cast

3. whisk — whist   6. risk — wrist

5 **Word Building: Compound Words.** Build the compound words below. All of these words are closed compounds.

1. task + master _____   6. sales + clerk _____

2. camp + ground _____   7. out + cast _____

3. clock + work _____   8. hand + clasp _____

4. break + fast _____   9. team + work _____

5. color + fast _____   10. fore + most _____

Use three of these words in sentences. Look up the words in a dictionary if necessary.

1. _____

2. _____

3. _____

6 **The Suffixes -*er* and -*est*.** The suffixes -*er* and -*est* are added to adjectives and adverbs to show comparisons.

Part A: Study these examples and fill in the blanks in the pattern which follows.

-er	*-est*
1. This desk is *bigger* than that one.	This is the *biggest* house on the block.
2. We're *closer* to home than we were.	Tonight he came the *closest* to winning.
3. Your mask is *scarier* than mine.	She wore the *scariest* mask I've ever seen.

Pattern: When two things are being compared, add the suffix _____.

When three or more things are being compared, add the suffix _____.

Part B: Add the suffixes to the words below. Follow the patterns that you have studied for adding endings.

1. slim + er   _____

2. bumpy + est _____

3. brave + est _____

4. costly + er _____

5. blue + er   _____

6. crunchy + est _____

7. flat + er   _____

8. pretty + er _____

9. strange + est _____

10. crusty + er _____

Part C: On the lines below, write the phrases that you hear. Remember to follow the patterns that you have learned for adding endings.

1. _____

2. _____

3. _____

4. _____

5. _____

6. _____

7. _____

8. _____

9. _____

10. _____

7 **More about Comparisons**

Part A: Write the root word for each of the words below and answer the question that follows.

1. damper _____   5. shadiest _____

2. fastest _____   6. brighter _____

3. emptier _____   7. crisper _____

4. craziest _____   8. thirstier _____

How many syllables do the root words have? _____ or _____

Part B: Study the examples below and answer the question.

Comparing two things: 1. This sunset is *more beautiful* than the one last night.
2. Is this game *more important* than next week's game?

Comparing three or more things: 1. These are the *most beautiful* flowers in the garden.
2. This is the *most important* interview I've had.

How many syllables do *beautiful* and *important* have? _____

Now fill in the blanks in the pattern below.

Pattern: The suffixes _____ and _____ are usually added to words with one

or two syllables to show comparison.

The words _____ and _____ are usually used with words of

three or more syllables to show comparison.

8 **Writing Sentences.** On the lines below, write the sentences that you hear.

1. _____

2. _____

3. _____

4. _____

5. _____

Lesson 14

The Blends *lt*, *ld*, and *lm*

Sight Words		
world	captain	worth
soldier	sergeant	forth

Blends

❶ Listening

lt   Listen to the sound of *lt* in these words.

belt	wilt	colt	result
felt	built	adult	consult
melting	quilt	saltiest	difficult

ld   Listen to the sound of *ld* in these words.

bold	child	field
behold	rebuild	golden
foretold	building	shoulder

lm   Listen to the sound of *lm* in these words.

elm	helm	realm
film	helmet	overwhelm

❷ Writing Words. On the lines below, write the words that you hear.

1. _____   4. _____   7. _____

2. _____   5. _____   8. _____

3. _____   6. _____   9. _____

3 **Using Sight Words.** Fill in each blank in the sentences below with one of the sight words from this lesson. Use each word only once.

1. A person in the army is called a _____.

2. A _____ has a higher rank than a sergeant.

3. A _____ has a higher rank than a private.

4. Frank bought three dollars' _____ of gasoline.

5. The Chases took a cruise around the _____.

6. Who was the first to come _____ when the captain asked for volunteers?

4 **Word Building.** Write one of the blends from this lesson in each of the blanks below to form a word. Do not make the same word twice.

1. bo _____   6. fi _____   11. mi _____

2. bo _____   7. gui _____   12. mo _____

3. co _____   8. ha _____   13. sco _____

4. co _____   9. he _____   14. ti _____

5. e _____   10. jo _____   15. yie _____

5 **Homonyms That End in /ld/.** Words that end in *ld* often sound like the past tense of words that end with *l*. Choose the correct word in each of the sentences below and write it on the line provided. Use your dictionary if you need to.

1. Glenn (bold/bowled) very well last night.   _____

2. A (bald/balled) eagle has white feathers on its head.   _____

3. Hope (weld/welled) up in Grace's heart.   _____

4. I (told/tolled) Kent to go home.   _____

5. Pris's boots needed to be (resold/resoled).   _____

6. Who (build/billed) you for the repairs?   _____

6 **Reviewing the Apostrophe.** Write the phrases and sentences that you hear. Use an apostrophe when necessary.

1. _____   6. _____

2. _____   7. _____

3. _____   8. _____

4. _____   9. _____

5. _____   10. _____

7 **Word Building: Compound Words.** Build the compound words below. All of these are closed compounds.

1. with + hold _____   6. film + strip _____

2. film + goer _____   7. ten + fold _____

3. up + hold _____   8. thunder + bolt _____

4. salt + box _____   9. worth + while _____

5. helms + man _____   10. house + hold _____

Use two of these compound words in sentences.

1. _____

2. _____

8 **Writing Sentences.** On the lines below, write the sentences that you hear.

1. _____

2. _____

3. _____

4. _____

5. _____

9 **Puzzle.** Use the clues below to fill in the blocks of the puzzle. Refer to the list of answer words at the bottom of the page if you need to. When you have filled in all the correct answers, the letters in the shaded blocks will spell a military rank between sergeant and captain.

Clues

1. A structure for living or working in

2. A person who serves in an army

3. Changing from solid to liquid by heating

4. Where the arm attaches to the body

5. Units used to measure electricity

6. People who live under the same roof

7. The color of a metal used for jewelry

8. Grown up

9. Making a motion picure

10. An officer in the army

The military rank: _____

Word List

adult
building
captain
filming
golden
household
melting
shoulder
soldier
volts

Lesson 15

The Blends *lk*, *lp*, and *lf*

Sight Words		
folk	look	down
yolk	listen	bought

Blends

lk

lp

lf

1 Listening

Listen to the sound of *lk* in these words.

elk	hulk	silk
bulk	sulking	buttermilk

Listen to the sound of *lp* in these words.

help	gulps	pulp
helper	scalp	pulpiness

Listen to the sound of *lf* in these words.

shelf	wolf	gulf
selfish	golfing	engulf

2 **Writing Words.** On the lines below, write the words that you hear.

1. _____   4. _____   7. _____

2. _____   5. _____   8. _____

3. _____   6. _____   9. _____

3 **Using Sight Words.** Use one of the sight words from this lesson to complete each sentence.

1. Gramps _____ a new suit to wear to the wedding.

2. A chicken egg is made up of the white and the _____.

3. Did the boss _____ at Phyllis's progress report?

4. I love to _____ to the talk shows on the radio.

5. Ralph played the guitar and sang _____ songs at the party.

6. All the decorations had to be taken _____ after the holidays.

4 **Adding -s or -es to Words That End in lf.** Some words that end in *lf* change the *f* to *v* before *-es* is added. For verbs that end in *lf* and for a few nouns also, the *f* is kept and *-s* is added. Add *-s* or *-es* to the words below. Use your dictionary when necessary.

1. self   _____   5. shelf   _____

2. half   _____   6. wolf   _____

3. elf   _____   7. gulf   _____

4. golf   _____   8. engulf _____

5 **Using the Dictionary: Compound Words with Self.** Make the compound words indicated. Use your dictionary to determine whether they should be closed, open, or hyphenated compounds.

1. self + conscious _____   5. self + made   _____

2. self + supporting _____   6. self + doubt   _____

3. self + pity   _____   7. self + control _____

4. self + respect   _____   8. self + help   _____

All of these words have a _____ between the two parts.

6 **Creating Sentences.** Write sentences using the words that are formed by adding *self* to the personal pronouns.

1. myself: _____

2. yourself: _____

3. himself: _____

4. herself: _____

5. itself: _____

6. ourselves: _____

7. yourselves: _____

8. themselves: _____

7 **Writing Words by Syllables.** Write each word your teacher dictates by syllables. Then write the whole word on the line provided.

First Syllable	Second Syllable	Third Syllable	Fourth Syllable	Whole Word
1. _____	_____	_____		_____
2. _____	_____	_____		_____
3. _____	_____	_____		_____
4. _____	_____	_____	_____	_____
5. _____	_____	_____	_____	_____
6. _____	_____	_____	_____	_____
7. _____	_____	_____	_____	_____
8. _____	_____	_____	_____	_____

Use two of these words in sentences.

1. _____

2. _____

8 Finding Root Words. Write the root word for each of the words below.

1. silkiest _____

2. unclasped _____

3. behalf _____

4. assistance _____

5. diskette _____

6. milkiness _____

7. shelving _____

8. unmasked _____

9. bulkiness _____

10. resulting _____

11. unhelpful _____

12. rebuilding _____

9 Review of Comparisons. Fill in the blank in each sentence below with the correct form of the word in parentheses.

1. (risky) Jack's stunt is _____ than Fred's.

2. (hot) Today is the _____ day we've had all summer.

3. (funny) Chris's joke was _____ than the one Grant told.

4. (spectacular) That was the _____ stunt I've ever seen.

5. (safe) They tried to make the race course _____ than it was.

6. (suspicious) That letter was the _____ clue the detective found.

10 Writing Sentences. On the lines below, write the sentences that you hear.

1. _____

2. _____

3. _____

4. _____

_____

5. _____

_____

Lesson 16

The Blends *ct*, *ft*, *pt*, and *xt*

Sight Words		
indict	sample	ghost
example	simple	ghetto

Blends

1 **Listening**

ct

Listen to the sound of *ct* in these words.

act	affect	strict	elected
exact	object	district	direct
react	perfect	verdict	connect
attract	intellect	suspect	contract

ft

Listen to the sound of *ft* in these words.

gift	lift	raft	soft
sift	drift	draft	left
swift	thrifty	handicraft	theft

pt

Listen to the sound of *pt* in these words.

apt	kept	accept	prompt
adapt	slept	concept	abrupt
adopt	Egypt	attempt	interrupt

xt

Listen to the sound of *xt* in these words.

next	text	context

2 **Writing Words.** On the lines below, write the words that you hear.

1. _____   4. _____   7. _____

2. _____   5. _____   8. _____

3. _____   6. _____   9. _____

3 **Word Building with the Suffix -ion.** In Lesson 6 you learned that nouns can be formed from verbs by adding the suffix -tion. When the verb ends in *ct* or *pt*, the suffix -ion is usually added to form the noun.

Build these words and answer the question below. Use the dictionary to check your spellings.

1. adopt + ion _____

2. connect + ion _____

3. except + ion _____

4. infect + ion _____

5. affect + ion _____

6. act + ion _____

7. erupt + ion _____

8. restrict + ion _____

9. elect + ion _____

10. disrupt + ion _____

If you hear /k/ or /p/ before /shən/, how is the /shən/ spelled? _____

4 **Adding Suffixes.** Add one of the suffixes below to each of these words. Remember that sometimes the root word changes or other letters are added before you add the suffix. Pronounce the new word before you spell it. Use the dictionary to check your spellings.

-ion   -cian   -sion   -tion

1. interrupt _____

2. explain _____

3. react _____

4. confess _____

5. educate _____

6. adapt _____

7. object _____

8. create _____

9. expect _____

10. beauty _____

11. permit _____

12. contract _____

13. concept _____

14. electric _____

15. perfect _____

16. complicate _____

17. transport _____

18. televise _____

19. subtract _____

20. translate _____

5 **Word Building: Compound Words.** Match a word from Column 2 with each word in Column 1 to make a compound word. Use each word in Column 1 only once. Check your dictionary to see if the compounds are closed, hyphenated, or open.

Column 1	Column 2		Compound Words	
air	book	1. _____	6. _____
crank	craft		
drift	drift	2. _____	7. _____
fork	drink		
left	hand	3. _____	8. _____
make	lift		
snow	shaft	4. _____	9. _____
soft	shift		
spend	thrift	5. _____	10. _____
text	wood		

Use three of the compound words in sentences.

1. _____

2. _____

3. _____

6 **Dictionary Skills: Finding the Correct Spelling.** The blend *ct* at the end of a word sounds like the past tense of words that end in *ck*. Use the dictionary to find the correct spellings of the words spelled phonetically below. When you find the spelling that matches the meaning, write the word in the appropriate column.

Phonetic Spelling	Meaning	-ct	-cked
1. /ĭn sĕkt´/	a small animal with six legs	_____	_____
2. /ă tăkt´/	began a battle	_____	_____
3. /dē fĕkt´/	a fault or flaw	_____	_____
4. /ĭn flĭkt´/	to strike; to impose	_____	_____
5. /flĭkt/	removed with a quick motion	_____	_____
6. /ĭn spĕkt´/	to examine carefully	_____	_____

7 **Writing Sentences.** On the lines below, write the sentences that you hear.

1. _____

2. _____

3. _____

4. _____

5. _____
_____

6. _____
_____

8 **Composing a Paragraph.** On a separate sheet of paper, write a paragraph of five or six sentences about the scene below. Use some of the listed words in your paragraph.

attempt	district	interrupt	react
conduct	exact	objection	suspect
direct	indict	prompt	verdict

Lesson 17

The Blends *rd*, *rm*, *rn*, *rb*, and *rf*

Sight Words			
bird	earn	herb	worm
word	learn	sword	wharf

Blends

1 Listening

rd

Listen to the sound of *rd* in these words.

cord	herd	third	aboard
chord	heard	regard	toward
afford	hurdle	hardly	forward

rm

Listen to the sound of *rm* in these words.

harm	warm	germ	storm
alarm	warmth	midterm	uniform
disarm	swarming	firmly	transform

rn

Listen to the sound of *rn* in these words.

barn	fern	torn	turn
warn	concern	tornado	burned
worn	lantern	cornfield	adornment

rb

Listen to the sound of *rb* in these words.

curb	verb	superb
garb	adverb	suburb
garbage	proverb	disturb

rf

Listen to the sound of *rf* in these words.

surf	turf	dwarf
surface	surfboard	scarf

2 **Writing Words.** On the lines below, write the words that you hear.

1. _____   5. _____   9. _____

2. _____   6. _____   10. _____

3. _____   7. _____   11. _____

4. _____   8. _____   12. _____

3 **Word Building.** Add three of the endings below to each word.

able	ed	ing	ness
al	er	less	y
ance	ful	ly	

1. firm _____ _____ _____

2. harm _____ _____ _____

3. form _____ _____ _____

4. storm _____ _____ _____

5. surf _____ _____ _____

6. disturb _____ _____ _____

7. afford _____ _____ _____

8. warm _____ _____ _____

9. regard _____ _____ _____

10. hard _____ _____ _____

11. charm _____ _____ _____

12. inform _____ _____ _____

13. forward _____ _____ _____

14. transform _____ _____ _____

15. perform _____ _____ _____

4 **Review of Syllable Types.** Write two other examples of each of the syllable types listed below.

Syllable Type	Example	Your Examples	
closed	curb	_____	_____
open	go	_____	_____
Cle	ble	_____	_____
double vowel	steel	_____	_____
VCe	fine	_____	_____

5 **Writing Words by Syllables.** Write each word your teacher dictates by syllables. Then write the whole word on the line provided.

	First Syllable	Second Syllable	Third Syllable	Fourth Syllable	Whole Word
1.	_____	_____			_____
2.	_____	_____	_____		_____
3.	_____	_____	_____		_____
4.	_____	_____	_____	_____	_____
5.	_____	_____	_____		_____
6.	_____	_____	_____	_____	_____

Now write these five-syllable words:

7. _____ _____ _____ _____ _____   _____

8. _____ _____ _____ _____ _____   _____

Use three of the words you wrote in sentences.

1. _____

2. _____

3. _____

6 **Using Words with Many Syllables.** Fill in the blanks in the sentences with the words listed below. Use each word only once.

aspirations   confirmation   difficulties
attraction   consultation   transformation

1. Did you receive a _____ of your airline reservations?

2. The roller coaster is the main _____ at the amusement park.

3. Herb has _____ toward becoming a professional baseball player.

4. Trudy has undergone a complete _____ since she started her exercise program.

5. Carl has a _____ with Dr. Jenkins tomorrow to discuss his operation.

6. The Campbells ran into a great many _____ when they were remodeling their house.

7 **Dictionary Skills: Homonyms.** Use your dictionary to help you choose the correct word from each homonym pair in parentheses. Write the correct words on the lines provided.

1. Do you think Stan (heard/herd) what I said?   _____

2. That old washcloth is all (warn/worn) out.   _____

3. Herb is raising a (heard/herd) of sheep.   _____

4. He played several (cords/chords) to try out the guitar.   _____

5. Why did Frank (warn/worn) you not to go there?   _____

8 **Writing Sentences.** On the lines below, write the sentences that you hear.

1. _____

2. _____

3. _____

4. _____

5. _____

Lesson 18

The Blends *rt*, *rl*, *rk*, *rse*, *rce*, and *rp*

Sight Words		
source	pearl	warp
resource	corps	worse

Blends

1 Listening

rt

Listen to the sound of *rt* in these words.

shirt	alert	port	part
skirt	expert	sport	quart
dirty	inverted	comfort	forty

rl

Listen to the sound of *rl* in these words.

girl	curl	hurl
swirl	purl	whirl
twirling	unfurled	snarl

rk

Listen to the sound of *rk* in these words.

dark	remark	fork	network
park	postmark	pork	housework

rse

Listen to the sound of *rse* in these words.

coarse	verse	curse	sparse
course	reverse	nurses	endorse
horse	converse	purse	rehearse
hoarse	disperse	reimburse	discourse

rce

Listen to the sound of *rce* in these words.

scarce	force	divorced	fierce
scarcely	enforce	reinforce	pierce

rp

Listen to the sound of *rp* in these words.

burp	harp	sharp	chirping

2 **Writing Words.** On the lines below, write the words that you hear.

1. _____ 5. _____ 9. _____

2. _____ 6. _____ 10. _____

3. _____ 7. _____ 11. _____

4. _____ 8. _____ 12. _____

3 **Using Sight Words.** Use one of the sight words from this lesson to complete each sentence.

1. Jane has a string of _____ that belonged to her grandmother.

2. The U.S. Army Air _____ became the U.S. Air Force.

3. If managed, forests are a renewable natural _____.

4. Trees are a common _____ for the pulp used to make paper.

5. The patient is feeling _____ today than he was yesterday.

6. If you let that wood get wet, it will _____.

4 **Word Building with Silent _e_ Patterns.** Review Silent _e_ Patterns 1 and 2 and then add the endings to the words below.

Pattern 1: The final silent _e_ is dropped from a word when an ending that begins with a vowel is added.

Pattern 2: When an ending that begins with _a_ or _o_ is added to a word that ends in _ce_ or _ge_, the silent _e_ is kept to retain the soft _c_ and _g_ sounds.

1. scarce + ity _____   7. enforce + able _____

2. force + ing _____   8. reverse + ible _____

3. reverse + al _____   9. resource + ful _____

4. fierce + ly _____   10. pierce + ing _____

5. worse + en _____   11. nurse + ery _____

6. disperse + al _____   12. reinforce + able _____

5 **Dictionary Skills: Finding the Correct Spelling.** The sound /rs/ at the end of a word can be spelled *rce* or *rse*. Use the dictionary to find the correct spellings of the words spelled phonetically below. When you find the spelling that matches the meaning, write the word in the appropriate column.

Phonetic Spelling	Meaning	rce	rse
1. /ăd vŭrs´/	harmful; unfavorable; opposing	_____	_____
2. /färs/	a ridiculous action or situation	_____	_____
3. /rē mŏrs´/	great regret	_____	_____
4. /tĕrs/	short and to the point	_____	_____
5. /kŏm´ ərs/	the buying and selling of goods	_____	_____
6. /dĭ vŭrs´/	distinctly different from each other	_____	_____
7. /dĭs bŭrs´/	to pay out from a fund	_____	_____
8. /ĭn vŭrs´/	reversed in order or effect	_____	_____

Notice how many words you wrote in each column. *Rse* is a more common spelling than *rce*. There are almost three times as many words spelled with *rse* as there are words spelled with *rce*.

6 **Dictionary Skills: Homonyms.** Use each of the homonyms below in a sentence. Look up the meanings in the dictionary if necessary.

1. coarse _____

2. course _____

3. hoarse _____

4. horse _____

5. core _____

6. corps _____

7 **Writing Sentences.** On the lines below, write the sentences that you hear.

1. _____

2. _____

3. _____

4. _____

5. _____

6. _____

8 **Puzzle.** Use the clues below to fill in the blocks of the puzzle. All of the answers are representative words or sight words in this lesson. When you have filled in all the correct answers, the shaded blocks will spell a new word ending in *rse*.

Clues

1. to throw something with force

2. to add strength to something

3. to make a hole in something

4. turn backward or change direction

5. turned upside down

6. rough; not smooth or fine

7. the origin or beginning of something

8. a highly skilled person

The new word: _____

On the line below, write a sentence using the new word.

_____

Review of Unit 5

Blends That End Syllables

1 **Word Building.** Write one of the blends below in each blank to make a word. Do not make the same word twice.

mp   st   sp   sk   lt   ld   lm   lk   lp.   lf   ct   ft   pt   xt

1. ba_____
2. ba_____
3. cla_____
4. cra_____
5. cre_____
6. cru_____
7. de_____

8. exa_____
9. gra_____
10. he_____
11. he_____
12. hu_____
13. ke_____
14. mi_____

15. ne_____
16. ne_____
17. pa_____
18. sta_____
19. ti_____
20. wa_____
21. wo_____

2 **Spelling Words That End in /shən/.** Answer the questions below.

1. Write three ways you have learned to spell /shən/ at the end of words.

_____   _____   _____

2. What is the most common spelling of /shən/? _____

3. When the root verb ends in *ct* or *pt*, _____ is added to form the noun.

4. When you hear /k/ or /p/ before /shən/ at the end of a word, how will the /shən/

   be spelled? _____

Write the correct spelling of /shən/ on the lines below.

1. attrac_____
2. recep_____
3. profes_____

4. adop_____
5. musi_____
6. infec_____

7. admis_____
8. connec_____
9. discus_____

3 **Review of Silent *e* Pattern 2.** Fill in the blanks to complete the pattern below.

Pattern: When an ending that begins with ____ or ____ is added to a word that ends in *ce* or *ge*, the silent *e* is kept to retain the soft ____ and ____ sounds.

Add the endings to the words below. Keep the silent *e* when necessary.

1. enforce + able _____

2. force + ible _____

3. pierce + ing _____

4. outrage + ous _____

5. dance + ing _____

6. reverse + al _____

7. reverse + ible _____

8. fierce + ly _____

9. entrance + ing _____

10. recharge + able _____

4 **Review of the *-er* and *-est* Suffixes.** The suffixes *-er* and *-est* are added to adjectives and adverbs to show comparison. Fill in the blanks below to review how they are used.

1. The *-er* ending is used when _____ things are being compared.

2. The *-est* ending is used when _____ or more things are being compared.

3. *-Er* and *-est* are usually added to words of _____ or _____ syllables.

4. The words _____ and _____ are usually used with words of three or more syllables to show comparison.

Write the phrases you hear on the lines below.

1. _____

2. _____

3. _____

4. _____

5. _____

6. _____

7. _____

8. _____

9. _____

10. _____

5 **Word Building: Compound Words.** Match a word from Column 2 with each word in Column 1 to make a compound word. Use each word in Column 1 only once. Check your dictionary to find whether the compounds are closed, hyphenated, or open.

Column 1	Column 2		Compound Words
adult	bird	1. _____	9. _____
folk	boiled		
fore	burly	2. _____	10. _____
ghost	cellar		
hard	craft	3. _____	11. _____
heart	door		
help	felt	4. _____	12. _____
hurly	fish		
left	hood	5. _____	13. _____
next	mate		
silk	over	6. _____	14. _____
song	pike		
space	singer	7. _____	15. _____
storm	town		
sword	word	8. _____	16. _____
turn	worm		

6 **Alternative Spellings for /ld/ and /kt/.** Write the phrases you hear.

1. _____   5. _____

2. _____   6. _____

3. _____   7. _____

4. _____   8. _____

7 **Reviewing Homonyms.** Select the correct word in each sentence and write it on the line provided.

1. Of (coarse/course) Frank can fix your fence. _____

2. You'll have to tie that package with strong (chord/cord). _____

3. Have you (heard/herd) the news? _____

4. Did you (warn/worn) him not to go into the street? _____

5. Clark's cold made his voice (hoarse/horse). _____

8 **Word Building: Alternative Spellings for /rs/.** Fill in the blanks in the sentences below with *rse* or *rce*. Remember that *rse* is the more common spelling.

1. If you will endo____ ____ ____ this check, I'll deposit it.

2. A referee's job is to enfo____ ____ ____ the rules of the game.

3. As soon as I got to the doctor's office, a nu____ ____ ____ took my temperature.

4. Fred forgot the third ve____ ____ ____ of the song he was singing.

5. There was a very spa____ ____ ____ crowd at the fair because of the rain.

6. Did Mr. Wolf reimbu____ ____ ____ you for the money you spent fixing his faucet?

7. My grandmother used to say things were "as sca____ ____ ____ as hen's teeth."

8. Grandmother also used to say, "You can lead a ho____ ____ ____ to water, but you can't make him drink."

9 **Finding Root Words.** Write the root word for each word below.

1. comfortable _____

2. adaptation _____

3. disarmament _____

4. unfurled _____

5. costliest _____

6. transformation _____

7. conversation _____

8. consultation _____

9. expectation _____

10. unselfishness _____

10 **Writing Sentences.** On the lines below, write the sentences that you hear.

1. _____

2. _____

3. _____

4. _____

5. _____

_____

11 **Composing Sentences.** On the lines provided, write two or three sentences about each picture below. Use some of the representative words and sight words from Unit 5 in your sentences.

_____
_____
_____
_____
_____

_____
_____
_____
_____
_____

12 **Crossword Puzzle.** Use the clues below to complete this crossword puzzle. Most of the answers are representative words or sight words from Unit 5 or contain Unit 5 blends.

Across

1. Bothers; annoys: ___ the peace
5. Past tense of feel
7. A place for growing crops
9. A warning sound; a signal
10. To break into a conversation
12. Grassy soil; sod
13. Not good enough to be approved
16. A young horse
18. A possessive personal pronoun
20. To accuse of a crime
22. Try
23. A yellowish color

Down

1. A problem or hardship; something that must be overcome
2. Was asleep
3. Abbreviation for road
4. Opposite of dull; a ___ knife
5. Predicted; forecast
6. Careful about money
8. Give orders or directions
11. Browning bread or marshmallows
14. Sudden; all at once
15. On time
17. An animal that can fly
19. Short for Samuel
21. Five plus five

Lesson 19

The Silent Partners *mb*, *mn*, *lm*, and *lk*

<table>
<tr><td colspan="3" align="center">Sight Words</td></tr>
<tr><td>psalm</td><td>soften</td><td>wherever</td></tr>
<tr><td>often</td><td>softener</td><td>threshold</td></tr>
</table>

Silent Partners

1 Listening

mb

Listen to the sound of *mb* in these words.

lamb	comb	numb	dumb
limb	womb	crumb	dumbwaiter
climb	bombshell	plumber	thumbnail

mn

Listen to the sound of *mn* in these words.

hymn	column	condemn
autumn	solemn	condemned

lm

Listen to the sound of *lm* in these words.

calm	balm	qualm
palm	embalm	Malcolm

lk

Listen to the sound of *lk* in these words.

talk	walk	folk	yolk
stalk	crosswalk	folklore	chalk

Underline the silent consonants in the representative words above.

2 **Writing Words.** On the lines below, write the words that you hear.

1. _____ 5. _____ 9. _____

2. _____ 6. _____ 10. _____

3. _____ 7. _____ 11. _____

4. _____ 8. _____ 12. _____

3 **Silent Consonants.** Sometimes when *mb*, *mn*, *lm*, and *lk* occur in words, one consonant in each pair is silent. In some words, both consonants can be heard.

Underline the silent consonants in the words below. If all the consonants can be heard, underline the whole word. Use your dictionary to check the pronunciation, if necessary.

mb	mn	lm	lk
1. mumble	6. condemn	11. elm	16. balk
2. succumb	7. dimness	12. palm	17. silky
3. tomb	8. autumn	13. film	18. talking
4. climber	9. chimney	14. helmet	19. bulkier
5. September	10. warmness	15. calmness	20. chalky

Now fill in the blanks below.

1. If one consonant is silent in the pair *mb*, it is usually the _____.

2. If one consonant is silent in the pair *mn*, it is usually the _____.

3. If one consonant is silent in the pair *lm*, it is usually the _____.

4. If one consonant is silent in the pair *lk*, it is usually the _____.

4 **Dictionary Skills: Silent Consonants.** Some words that contain a silent consonant have related words in which that consonant is pronounced. Learning these words can help you to remember the silent consonant in the root or related word.

Look up the word *columnist* in the dictionary. Write the pronunciation and meaning below.

columnist _____

_____

Remembering the word *columnist* can help you remember the silent *n* in the word *column*.

Now look up the words below in your dictionary. For each word, find a related word in which the silent consonant is pronounced. Write the related words and their meanings on the lines provided.

Related Word	**Meaning**
1. autumn _____	_____
2. hymn _____	_____
3. bomb _____	_____
4. crumb _____	_____
5. soften _____	_____
6. condemn _____	_____
7. solemn _____	_____

Now choose three pairs of silent-consonant and related words and use each of the pairs in a sentence. See the example below.

Example: *Autumn* begins with the *autumnal* equinox.

1. _____

2. _____

3. _____

5 **Mnemonics.** Look up the word *mnemonic* in your dictionary. Write the pronunciation and the definition on the lines below.

mnemonic _____

_____

Mnemonics help us to remember things. For instance, you can distinguish between the homonyms *here* and *hear* if you remember that *hear* has the word *ear* in it.

Mnemonics can also help you to remember how to spell words that contain silent consonants. These mnemonics can be either phrases or sentences that link the silent-consonant word with a word you know how to spell.

Example: *Dumbo* was not a *dumb* elephant.

The best mnemonics are ones that you develop yourself. Make up mnemonics for any of the following words that you have trouble spelling.

1. climb _____

2. palm _____

3. numb _____

4. plumber _____

5. limb _____

6. thumb _____

7. stalk _____

6 **Writing Sentences.** On the lines below, write the sentences that you hear.

1. _____

2. _____

3. _____

4. _____

5. _____

Lesson 20

The Silent Partners *gn*, *kn*, *wr*, and *stle*

Sight Words	
reign	isle
foreign	aisle
Lincoln	island

Silent Partners

❶ Listening

gn

Listen to the sound of *gn* in these words.

gnat	sign	align	assign
gnaw	resign	benign	assignment
gnash	designing	campaign	

kn

Listen to the sound of *kn* in these words.

know	knit	knee	kneeling
knew	knot	knock	unknown
known	knob	knuckle	knowledge

wr

Listen to the sound of *wr* in these words.

write	wreck	awry	wrapper
wrote	wring	wrist	wriggle
written	wrong	wrinkle	playwright

stle

Listen to the sound of *stle* in these words.

bustle	bristle	castle
hustle	whistle	jostle
rustle	thistle	wrestle

2 Writing Words. On the lines below, write the words that you hear.

1. _____   5. _____   9. _____

2. _____   6. _____   10. _____

3. _____   7. _____   11. _____

4. _____   8. _____   12. _____

3 Silent Consonants. Usually when the consonant pairs in this lesson occur in words, one consonant of each pair is silent. Pronounce each word in Exercise 1 and underline each silent consonant. Then fill in the blanks in the statements below.

1. In the consonant pair *gn*, the consonant _____ is usually silent.

2. In the consonant pair *kn*, the consonant _____ is usually silent.

3. In the consonant pair *wr*, the consonant _____ is usually silent.

4. In the group *stle*, the consonant _____ is usually silent.

5. The consonant pair _____ occurs at both the beginning and end of syllables.

6. The consonant pairs _____ and _____ occur only at the beginning of syllables.

4 Dictionary Skills: Silent Consonants. In Lesson 19 you learned that some words that contain a silent consonant have related words in which that consonant is pronounced. These related words can help you remember the silent consonant in the root word. Look up the words below. For each word, find a related word in which the silent consonant is pronounced. Write the related words and their meanings on the lines provided.

	Related Word	**Meaning**
1. sign	_____	_____
2. design	_____	_____
3. malign	_____	_____
4. resign	_____	_____

5 **Mnemonics.** Mnemonics can be useful devices for remembering words that you have a great deal of trouble spelling. But you should develop mnemonics only when you really need them. Select four or five words from this lesson that you have trouble spelling and try to create mnemonics for them. Use the lines below.

      Word   **Mnemonic**

1. _____ _____
2. _____ _____
3. _____ _____
4. _____ _____
5. _____ _____

6 **Dictionary Skills: Homonyms.** Many words with silent letters have homonyms that are spelled differently. The meaning of the word in context will determine the correct spelling. Answer the questions below using a dictionary to check the meanings of the homonyms when necessary.

1. Is the passageway in a theater an *aisle* or an *isle*? _____

2. Do you *knead* or *need* the bread dough? _____

3. Is a recent purchase *knew* or *new*? _____

4. Did you *knot* or *not* the string? _____

5. Do you *know* or *no* how to do that puzzle? _____

6. Did King Arthur *rain* or *reign* long ago? _____

7. Do you *rap* or *wrap* a package? _____

8. Did the army *rest* or *wrest* power from the king? _____

9. Did the garbage *reek* or *wreak*? _____

10. Did you *ring* or *wring* out the laundry? _____

11. Was the bell *rung* or *wrung*? _____

12. Did you *rack* or *wrack* your brains for the answers? _____

7 **Dictionary Skills: Alternative Spellings for /səl/.** When a word ends in /səl/, it sounds like it ends in a Cle syllable. However, very few /səl/ words are spelled with *sle* at the end. Look up the words spelled phonetically below to find three different ways to spell /səl/. Write each word in the appropriate column below.

1. /věs′ əl/   a ship or large boat; a blood _____
2. /tŭs′ əl/   a rough struggle
3. /ĕ pĭs′ əl/   a long, formal letter
4. /chĭz′ əl/   a tool used to shape wood, stone, or metal
5. /hăs′ əl/   an argument or something troublesome
6. /grĭs′ əl/   a tough, stringy material that makes meat hard to chew
7. /pĕs′ əl/   a tool used for pounding or crushing something into powder
8. /tĭn′ səl/   glittering bits of foil or metal used for decorations
9. /trĕs′ əl/   a framework used to support railroad tracks or a road

stle	sel	sle
_____	_____	_____
_____	_____	_____
_____	_____	
_____		

The most common way to spell /səl/ at the end of a word is *stle*.

8 **Writing Sentences.** On the lines below, write the sentences that you hear.

1. _____
2. _____
3. _____
4. _____
5. _____
   _____
6. _____
   _____

Lesson 21

The Silent Partners *gh* and *ght*

```
┌─────────────────────────────────────────────┐
│                 Sight Words                   │
│     rough      cough      laugh              │
│     tough      trough     laughter           │
│     enough                                    │
└─────────────────────────────────────────────┘
```

Silent Partners

gh

ght

1 **Listening**

Listen for the sound of *gh* in these words.

high	nigh	though	bough
sigh	Hugh	through	dough
thigh	weigh	thorough	neighbor

Listen to the sound of *ght* in these words.

light	fight	bright	height
right	fought	frightened	weight
sight	taught	overnight	caught
tight	thought	straight	distraught

Underline the silent consonants in the representative words above.

2 **Writing Words.** On the lines below, write the words that you hear.

1. _____   5. _____   9. _____

2. _____   6. _____   10. _____

3. _____   7. _____   11. _____

4. _____   8. _____   12. _____

3 **Using Sight Words.** Fill in each blank with a sight word from this lesson. Use each word only once.

1. Herb's cold gave him a bad _____.

2. The horse took a long drink from the watering _____.

3. Norm sanded the _____ wood until it was smooth enough to paint.

4. Ronald had a _____ night, but he could _____ about it later.

5. The crowd's _____ was loud _____ to wake the neighbors.

4 **Dictionary Skills: Homonyms.** Underline the correct word in each sentence below. Use a dictionary to check the meanings when necessary.

1. He chose the (right/write) word.

2. Who (ate/eight) the last piece of pie?

3. A mole is an animal that (boroughs/burrows) in the ground.

4. Chuck said he (might/mite) be able to do the job.

5. Is he really going to go (threw/through) with it?

6. Ralph kneaded the (doe/dough) and then let it rise.

7. Dwight went (straight/strait) to work on the problem.

8. The sailors were (taught/taut) to keep the rope (taught/taut).

9. Do you (know/no) who (rote/wrote) the Bill of (Rights/Writes)?

10. King Arthur established the (Knights/Nights) of the Round Table.

11. The committee has selected a (sight/site) for the (knew/new) building.

12. Nurses (way/weigh) babies when they are born to find their birth (wait/weight).

5 **Word Building: Compound Words.** Form compound words using each of the words below. Check the dictionary to see if the compounds you form are closed, hyphenated, or open.

1. sight _____ 6. light _____

2. high _____ 7. night _____

3. dough _____ 8. rough _____

4. through _____ 9. tight _____

5. weight _____ 10. straight _____

6 **Choosing the Right Word.** Write one of the words listed below in each blank. Use each word only once.

        although   though   thought   thorough   throughout

Columbus was one of the early explorers who _____ the world was round. Before he sailed on his voyage of discovery, he did a _____ job of preparation. Columbus discovered America _____ he had been looking for a passage to the Indies. News of his discovery soon spread _____ Europe. Even _____ he discovered the Western Hemisphere, the American continents were not named after Columbus.

7 **Writing Sentences.** On the lines below, write the sentences that you hear.

1. _____

2. _____

3. _____

4. _____

_____

5. _____

_____

8 **Composing a Story.** Write a story about the events pictured below. Use some of the representative words and sight words from this unit.

_____

_____

_____

_____

_____

_____

_____

_____

_____

_____

_____

Review of Unit 6

The Silent Partners

1 **Word Building.** Write one of the silent partners below in each blank to make a word. Do not make the same word twice.

mb   mn   lm   lk   gn   kn   wr   stle   gh   ght

1. ba_____	9. ru_____	17. _____ash
2. cha_____	10. tau_____	18. _____at
3. cli_____	11. thou_____	19. _____eel
4. desi_____	12. thou_____	20. _____en
5. hei_____	13. throu_____	21. _____estle
6. hi_____	14. to_____	22. _____ight
7. hy_____	15. wa_____	23. _____ite
8. pa_____	16. whi_____	24. _____ot

2 **Review of the Related Words Strategy.** Underline the silent consonant in each word below. Then write a related word in which the consonant is pronounced.

Word	Related Word	Word	Related Word
1. sign	_____	7. condemn	_____
2. column	_____	8. resign	_____
3. autumn	_____	9. hymn	_____
4. bomb	_____	10. design	_____
5. solemn	_____	11. malign	_____
6. crumb	_____	12. soften	_____

3 Review of Silent Consonants

1. Write three words containing *mb* in which the *b* is silent.

_____   _____   _____

2. Write three words containing *mn* in which the *n* is silent.

_____   _____   _____

3. Write three words containing *lm* in which the *l* is silent.

_____   _____   _____

4. Write three words containing *lk* in which the *l* is silent.

_____   _____   _____

5. Write three words containing *gn* in which the *g* is silent.

_____   _____   _____

6. Write three words containing *kn* in which the *k* is silent.

_____   _____   _____

7. Write three words containing *wr* in which the *w* is silent.

_____   _____   _____

8. Write three words containing *stle* in which the *t* is silent.

_____   _____   _____

9. Write three words containing *gh* in which the *gh* is silent.

_____   _____   _____

10. Write three words containing *ght* in which the *gh* is silent.

_____   _____   _____

4 **Review of Homonyms.** Use each of the homonyms below in a sentence.

1. knot _____

   not _____

2. ring _____

   wring _____

3. wait _____

   weight _____

4. threw _____

   through _____

5. sight _____

   site _____

6. knew _____

   new _____

5 **Writing Sentences.** On the lines below, write the sentences that you hear.

1. _____

2. _____

3. _____

4. _____

5. _____

6. _____

   _____

7. _____

   _____

6 **Crossword Puzzle.** Use the clues below to complete this crossword puzzle. Most of the answers are representative words or sight words from Unit 6 or words that contain silent letters.

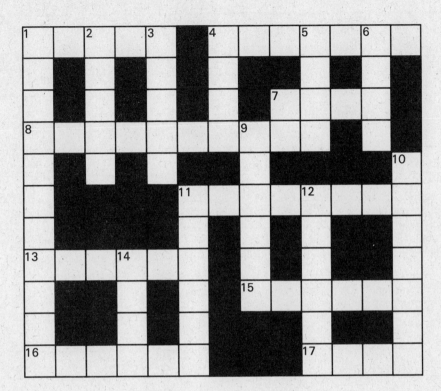

Across

1. Something that is seen: You are a ____ for sore eyes.
4. The person to call when your pipes leak
7. A small island
8. A task to be done; homework
11. Entirely complete: We gave the house a ____ cleaning.
13. A person who speaks a lot
15. The distance from the bottom to the top
16. To make soft
17. A sticky substance that holds things together

Down

1. Makes neat or straight
2. To grind the teeth
3. Not tender: This steak is ____.
4. A type of tropical tree
5. Has to: He ____ go home now.
6. What we see with
7. Opposite of out
9. Plenty; not too much
10. Blow through your lips: ____ while you work
11. A homonym of throne
12. Possessing
14. This ties two ropes together

Review of Book 3

Consonant Blends and Digraphs

Beginning Blends Lessons 1-5 and 9-10	Digraphs and Suffixes Lessons 6-8	Ending Blends Lessons 11-18	Silent Partners Lessons 19-21
bl, br			
cl, cr	ch, cian	ct	
dr			
fl, fr		ft	
gl, gr			gh, ght, gn
			kn
		ld, lf, lk, lm, lp, lt	lk, lm
		mp	mb, mn
		nd, ng, nk, nt, nce, nch, nge, nse	
pl, pr	ph	pt	
		rb, rd, rf, rk, rl, rm, rn, rp, rt, rce, rse	
sc, sk, sl, sm, sn, sp, st, sw, scr, shr, spl, spr, squ, str	sh, sion	sk, sp, st	stle
tr, tw, thr	th, tion, ture		
	wh		wr
		xt	

1 **Word Building.** Write one of the blends or digraphs above in each blank to form a word.

1. _____air
2. _____ate
3. _____ee
4. _____ere
5. _____ight
6. _____ind
7. _____ock
8. _____ore
9. bo_____
10. ca_____
11. cha_____
12. fo_____
13. mi_____
14. se_____
15. wi_____
16. wo_____

2 More Word Building. Add a word part from Column 2 to each blend or digraph in Column 1 to make a word. Write the words on the lines provided. Use each blend and digraph in Column 1 only once.

Column 1	Column 2		Words		
bl	ant	1. _____		6. _____	
ch	ild				
cr	ince	2. _____		7. _____	
fr	ink				
gr	ing	3. _____		8. _____	
pr	irt				
sk	ist	4. _____		9. _____	
spr	ost				
th	ough	5. _____		10. _____	
tw	unch				

3 Words That End in /shən/. Fill in the correct spelling of /shən/ to complete each of the words below and answer the questions that follow.

1. direc_____   5. addi_____   9. imagina_____

2. divi_____   6. televi_____   10. interrup_____

3. atten_____   7. pollu_____   11. musi_____

4. discus_____   8. objec_____   12. magi_____

What is the most common way to spell /shən/ at the end of words? _____

What is the ending that indicates a person skilled in some work? _____

If you hear /k/ or /p/ before /shən/, how is the /shən/ spelled? _____

4 Root Words. On the lines below, write the root word of each of the words in Exercise 3.

1. _____   5. _____   9. _____

2. _____   6. _____   10. _____

3. _____   7. _____   11. _____

4. _____   8. _____   12. _____

5 **Reviewing Patterns for Adding Endings.** Fill in the blanks below to review the patterns you have learned for adding endings.

1. **Doubling Pattern 1.** Double the final consonant if a word has one syllable, one _____, and one final _____, and the ending starts with a _____. Do not double _____ or *x*.

2. **Doubling Pattern 2.** If a word has more than one syllable, double the final consonant if the ending starts with a _____ and the last syllable has one _____, one final _____, and is accented.

3. **Silent *e* Pattern 1.** Drop the silent *e* at the end of a word if the ending begins with a _____.

4. **Silent *e* Pattern 2.** Do not drop the silent *e* at the end of a word that ends in *ce* or *ge* if the ending begins with _____ or _____.

5. **Changing *y* to *i*.** When adding an ending to a word that ends in C*y*, change the *y* to *i* unless the ending begins with _____. After changing the *y* to *i*, add _____ instead of *s* to nouns and verbs.

6. **Changing *f* to *v*.** To form the plural of some words that end in *f* or *fe*, change the *f* or *fe* to _____ and add _____.

Add the endings to the words below.

1. control + ed _____
2. rip + ing _____
3. begin + ing _____
4. dance + ing _____
5. forgot + en _____
6. notice + ed _____
7. notice + able _____
8. prosper + ed _____
9. ferry + s *or* es _____
10. hope + ing _____
11. change + able _____
12. wolf + s *or* es _____
13. worry + ing _____
14. self + s *or* es _____

6 **The Apostrophe.** Rewrite the phrases and sentences below adding the missing apostrophes.

1. Marys glasses _____

2. Two P.T.A.s were organized. _____

3. She cant help it. _____

4. the cities problems _____

5. the childrens party _____

6. I dont know. _____

7. several teachers classes _____

8. Arent you early? _____

9. his grandfathers beard _____

10. Jack wouldnt like it. _____

11. todays project _____

12. cross your ts _____

13. the womens sewing group _____

14. those companies policies _____

15. They havent been here. _____

7 **Reviewing the -er and -est Suffixes.** Fill in the blanks to complete the sentences below with the correct form of the word in parentheses. Remember to follow the spelling patterns you have studied.

1. (hungry) The baby was _____ than I thought she would be.

2. (dry) The weather this year has been _____ than last year.

3. (wet) Last April was the _____ month on record.

4. (juicy) Those oranges are _____ than the ones I bought.

5. (flat) That is the _____ tire I've ever seen.

8 **Reviewing Homonyms.** Write a sentence using each of the following homonyms.

1. principal _____

2. principle _____

3. right _____

4. write _____

5. there _____

6. their _____

7. forth _____

8. fourth _____

9. threw _____

10. through _____

11. worn _____

12. warn _____

9 **Review of Silent Consonant Strategies: Related Words and Mnemonics**

Part A: For each of the words below, write a related word that contains a silent consonant.

1. hymnal _____   6. crumble _____

2. signal _____   7. columnist _____

3. soft _____   8. designate _____

4. solemnity _____   9. resignation _____

5. bombard _____   10. condemnation _____

Part B: On the lines below, write a silent consonant word and a mnemonic that helps you remember how to spell it.

_____   _____

10 **Crossword Puzzle.** Use the clues below to complete this crossword puzzle. Most of the answers are representative words or sight words from Book 3.

Across

1. Tools similar to shears
5. The meal between breakfast and dinner
7. Makes plain; gives reasons for
8. A piece of furniture to sit on
10. Belonging to them
11. Wages or profits
13. Abbreviation for the United States
14. Scared; afraid
19. A knight's home
20. Without any faults
21. The metal from which steel is made
22. Citrus fruits
23. The opposite of difficult
24. The opposite of shorter
25. Small rivers

Down

1. Perfumed: The soap is heavily ____.
2. A person who serves in the army
3. Leaves out; fails to include
4. Someone that police think committed a crime
5. A document showing legal permission: a driver's ____
6. Plants used to season cooking
9. Your parent's sister
12. The present tense of ran
14. Style: That suit is in the latest ____.
15. "The grass is always ____ on the other side of the fence."
16. Hires; gives work to
17. Protection: "The best offense is a good ____."
18. People who create fine art
19. Coldness: I felt a ____ in the air.

Word Families and Representative Words

Lesson 1

bl
black
blame
blank
blanket
blaze
blend
bless
blotch
blow
blown
blue
bluff

cl
claim
clap
class
clean
clear
cliff
clip
clock
clutch

fl
flag
flame
flare
flat
fled
flee
fleet
flight
fling
flock
fluid
fly

gl
glad
glare
glass
gleam
glide
glove
glow
glue
glum

pl
complain

complete
employ
explain
explore
place
plan
plane
please
pledge
plenty
reply

Lesson 2

br
braid
brain
brake
brave
breakfast
brick
bridge
broke
broken
brush
February
library

cr
crack
cradle
crankcase
crayon
crazy
cream
creek
creep
crop
cross
crossing
cry

fr
afraid
frame
France
free
freeze
Friday
friend
fright
frog
frost

froze
San Francisco

gr
agree
grab
grade
grain
grand
grapes
grave
grease
green
greet
griddle
grill

Lesson 3

pr
April
improve
practice
praise
pray
preach
preparing
present
president
pretty
price
pride
prize
problem
program
surprise

tr
country
entrance
pantry
track
trade
tragedy
train
trap
travel
treat
tree
trick
trim
trip
truck
truly

dr
address
children
drag
dream
dress
drive
drop
drove
drug
drum
dry
hundred

Lesson 4

st
stable
stack
stain
stake
state
stay
steam
steel
stick
stiff
still
stitch
stock
stuck
study
stuff

sp
inspect
respect
space
spade
Spain
Spanish
speak
special
spell
spend
spice
spill

sn
snack
snail
snake
snap
sneak

sneeze
sniff
snore
snow

sl
slap
sled
sleep
sleeve
slice
slick
slide
slipper

sm
small
smear
smell
smile
smoke
smudge

Lesson 5

sc
scab
scale
scar
scarce
scare
scarlet
scatter
scold
score
scout
scuff
scum

sk
skating
skiing
skillet
skin
skip
skirt
skull
sky

sw
swam
swear
sweat
sweep

sweet
sweetheart
swell
swim
swimming
swing
Swiss
switch

tw
between
tweed
twelve
twenty
twenty-five
twice
twilight
twin
twine
twinkle
twist
twitch

Lesson 6

sh
blush
flesh
shacks
shady
shall
she
shears
shining
shoe
should
shoulder
wish

tion
action
addition
attention
donation
fiction
imagination
inflation
occupation
pollution
station
transportation
vacation

sion
admission
discussion
division
expression
permission
profession
session
television

cian
beautician
optician
magician
musician

Lesson 7

ph
alphabet
microphone
phobia
phone
phony
photograph
physical
physician
telephone

ch as /ch/
bleach
chain
chance
cheap
check
cheese
child
merchant
reach
rich
speech
teacher

ch as /k/
ache
anchor
chorus
character
chemical
Christmas
stomach
technical
technician

ture
adventure
agriculture
feature
fracture
lecture
mixture
nature
picture

Lesson 8

th as /th/
anything
athletic
bath
both
thank
thick
think
thirsty
thirteen
thunder
tooth
truth

th as /th/
brother
smooth
than
that
their
themselves
there
these
this
though
thus
together

wh
awhile
what
wheel
when
where
whether
which
whichever
whip
whistle
white
why

Lesson 9

str
strap

strange
stream
street
stretch
strike
string
strong
struck

scr
describe
description
inscription
scrap
scrape
scratch
scream
screen
scrub

spl
splash
splatter
splendid
splice
splinter
split

spr
sprain
spray
spree
spring
sprinkle
spry

Lesson 10

squ
squad
squall
squander
square
squat
squeak
squeal
squeamish
squeeze

shr
shrank
shred
shrill
shrimp
shrine
shrink
shrivel

shrub
shrunk

thr
three
threw
thrill
thrive
throat
throng
through
throw
thrust

Lesson 11

nd
bandage
bind
defend
find
fond
found
grandfather
handful
offend
pretend
remind
respond

nt
argument
aunt
cent
complaint
faint
important
infant
payment
pint
rent
sent
spent

nce
absence
announce
chance
convince
dance
difference
entrance
experience
fence
insurance
once
ounce

pronounce
residence
sentence
since

nse
defense
expense
license
offense
response
rinse
sense
tense

Lesson 12

ng
hanger
longing
nothing
rang
ring
rung
singer
standing
strongly
tongue
wrong
young

nk
bank
crankcase
ink
sank
shrank
sink
sunken
thankful
trunk

nch
branch
brunch
bunch
clinch
French
inch
lunch
munch
pinch
ranch
workbench
wrench

nge
angelfish

arrangement
challenge
changeable
cringe
exchange
fringe
hinge
lounge
lunge
orange
strangely

Lesson 13

mp
bump
camping
company
damp
empty
impish
pumpkin
slumping

sp
clasp
crisp
gasp
grasp
lisp
wasp

st
assist
cost
crust
dentist
fast
first
mostly
past

sk
ask
basketball
brisk
desk
disk
dusk
mask
risking

Lesson 14

lt
adult
belt
built

colt
consult
difficult
felt
melting
quilt
result
saltiest
wilt

ld
behold
bold
building
child
field
foretold
golden
rebuild
shoulder

lm
elm
film
helm
helmet
overwhelm
realm

Lesson 15

lk
bulk
buttermilk
elk
hulk
silk
sulking

lp
gulps
help
helper
pulp
pulpiness
scalp

lf
engulf
golfing
gulf
selfish
shelf
wolf

Lesson 16

ct
act
affect
attract
connect
contract
direct
district
elected
exact
intellect
object
perfect
react
strict
suspect
verdict

ft
draft
drift
gift
handicraft
left
lift
raft
sift
soft
swift
theft
thrifty

pt
abrupt
accept
adapt
adopt
apt
attempt
concept
Egypt
interrupt
kept
prompt
slept

xt
context
next
text

Lesson 17

rd
aboard
afford

chord
cord
forward
hardly
heard
herd
hurdle
regard
third
toward

rm
alarm
disarm
firmly
germ
harm
midterm
storm
swarming
transform
uniform
warm
warmth

rn
adornment
barn
burned
concern
cornfield
fern
lantern
torn
tornado
turn
warn
worn

rb
adverb
curb
disturb
garb
garbage
proverb
suburb
superb
verb

rf
dwarf
scarf
surf
surface
surfboard
turf

Lesson 18

rt
alert
comfort
dirty
expert
forty
inverted
part
port
quart
shirt
skirt
sport

rl
curl
girl
hurl
purl
snarl
swirl
twirling
unfurled
whirl

rk
dark
fork
housework
network
park
pork
postmark
remark

rse
coarse
converse
course
curse
discourse
disperse
endorse
hoarse
horse
nurses
purse
rehearse
reimburse
reverse
sparse
verse

rce
divorced
enforce

fierce
force
pierce
reinforce
scarce
scarcely

rp
burp
chirping
harp
sharp

Lesson 19

mb
bombshell
climb
comb
crumb
dumb
dumbwaiter
lamb
limb
numb
plumber
thumbnail
womb

mn
autumn
column
condemn
condemned
hymn
solemn

lm
balm
calm
embalm
Malcolm
palm
qualm

lk
chalk
crosswalk
folk
folklore
stalk
talk
walk
yolk

Lesson 20

gn
align

assign
assignment
benign
campaign
designing
gnash
gnat
gnaw
resign
sign

kn
knee
kneeling
knew
knit
knob
knock
knot
know
knowledge
known
knuckle
reknown

wr
awry
playwright
wrapper
wreck
wriggle
wring
wrinkle
wrist
write
written
wrong
wrote

stle
bristle
bustle
castle
hustle
jostle
rustle
thistle
whistle
wrestle

Lesson 21

gh
bough
dough
high
Hugh
neighbor

nigh
sigh
thigh
thorough
though
through
weigh

ght
bright
caught
distraught
fight
fought
frightened
height
light
overnight
right
sight
straight
taught
thought
tight
weight

Sight Words

Sight Word	Lesson Number	Sight Word	Lesson Number	Sight Word	Lesson Number
aisle	20	longer	12	thought	8
America	1	look	15	thread	10
billion	1	machine	7	threshold	19
bird	17	million	1	tough	21
bought	15	moist	13	trough	21
bruise	2	natural	7	view	11
build	2	necessary	4	warp	18
captain	14	ocean	6	wear	8
century	1	often	19	weather	8
cereal	4	onion	3	wharf	17
certain	4	pearl	18	wherever	19
chef	7	personal	13	whoever	8
chocolate	3	personnel	13	whose	8
clerk	13	psalm	19	word	17
corps	18	psychologist	7	work	13
cough	21	psychology	7	world	14
cruise	2	refrigerator	3	worm	17
cushion	6	reign	20	worse	18
down	15	resource	18	worth	14
earn	17	restaurant	11	yolk	15
England	12	review	11	younger	12
English	12	rough	21		
enough	21	salad	3		
example	16	sample	16		
fashion	6	scene	5		
finger	12	scent	5		
folk	15	schedule	5		
food	3	school	5		
foreign	20	science	5		
forth	14	scissors	5		
fruit	2	sergeant	14		
ghetto	16	shrewd	10		
ghost	16	shriek	10		
guard	11	simple	16		
guardian	11	soften	19		
herb	17	softener	19		
hoist	13	soldier	14		
house	1	source	18		
indict	16	spaghetti	3		
interview	11	spatula	7		
iron	1	spread	9		
island	20	squirrel	10		
isle	20	straight	9		
juice	2	strength	9		
laugh	21	sugar	6		
laughter	21	suit	2		
learn	17	sure	6		
Lincoln	20	suspicion	6		
linger	12	sword	17		
listen	15	Thomas	8		

My Personal Word List

Glossary of Terms

affix   A word element that carries meaning and is attached to a root word. Prefixes and suffixes are affixes; for example, *de-* and *-ful* in *delightful*.

blend   The joining together of two or more sounds with each sound still being heard; for example, /tr/ in *trade*.

C   A symbol representing any consonant.

compound word   A word formed by combining two or more words. Compound words can be closed (*greenhouse*), hyphenated (*red-letter*), or open (*yellow jacket*).

diacritical mark   A mark added to a letter to show how to pronounce the letter; for example, the straight line over a vowel to show a long vowel sound.

digraph   A pair of letters that represents one sound; for example, *ch* making the sound /ch/ in *chain* and *ea* making the sound /ē/ in *sea*.

family   A letter pattern or sequence such as *ine* in *fine, mine*, and *combine*. The pattern usually forms a common syllable ending and is composed of a vowel or vowel combination plus the consonant(s) that go with it.

homonym   One of a pair or more of words having the same sound but different meanings and often different spellings; for example, *tail* and *tale*.

pattern   A recurrent, usually predictable sequence of letters. Patterns occur in common syllables (e.g., *ope*) as well as in prefixes, suffixes, roots, and compound words. Spelling rules also produce patterns.

prefix   A word element that carries meaning and is attached to the beginning of a root word; for example, *pre-* in *prepaid*.

schwa   A vowel sound that usually occurs in unstressed syllables in English as heard in the first syllable of *against*; also the symbol (ə) often used to represent the sound.

sight word   A word that is not phonetically predictable; also any word for which students have not had the phonics to enable them to spell the word phonetically.

suffix   A word element that carries meaning and is attached to the end of a root word; for example, *-less* in *speechless*.

syllable   A spoken unit of uninterrupted sound containing one vowel sound producing either a word (e.g., *pay*) or a distinct part of a word (e.g., *pay* or *ment* in *payment*); the letters producing that sound in the word.

V   A symbol representing any vowel.

Style Notes

/x/ A letter between slashes indicates a sound rather than a spelling; for instance /b/ is the sound produced by the letter *b*.

/ĭ/ A curved mark (breve) over a vowel indicates the short vowel sound.

/ī/ A straight line (macron) over a vowel indicates the long vowel sound.

/ə/ This indicates the schwa sound.